AS THE RIVERS MERGE

AS THE
RIVERS
MERGE

A story of love, war and
perseverance across continents

DANIEL MAMAH

FISH EAGLE
PRESS

Copyright © 2024 by Daniel Mamah
www.mamah.com

Published in the United States by
Fish Eagle Press LLC, Saint Louis.

Library of Congress Control
Number: 2023952433

IISBN 979-8-9895124-5-4 (hardcover)
ISBN 979-8-9895124-2-3 (paperback)
ISBN 979-8-9895124-8-5 (ebook)

1   3   5   7   9   10   8   6   4   2

First Edition

To Caroline and Sophia

PREFACE

The idea of writing a book about my parents first emerged in 2012 when my wife, Thelma, was pregnant with our first child. Amid the emotion of the moment came the realization that my children would not build memories with their grandparents the way I did with mine. Instead, they would only know them through stories narrated by relatives. I remember growing up hearing about the lives of my great-grandparents this way and while I knew about where they lived and their vocations, my understanding of who they were was fundamentally superficial.

I had initially considered authoring a memoir recounting my experiences with my mother and father. However, I discovered a wealth of information from their distant past revealing a lot of their thoughts, feelings, struggles, and dreams. Such personal aspects of their lives could not be adequately captured with my voice; they had to be done through theirs. My mother communicated a lot in writing. Several hundreds of her handwritten letters were preserved by their recipients, primarily my aunts and grandmother, a few even dating back to the early 1950s when my mother was a young girl. On the other hand, my father religiously stored his official documents — from professional communications to receipts to informal notes. Reams of filled binders always lined his bookshelves. These were all reviewed to craft the storyline for this book, along with diaries, photographs, videos, historical texts, and interviews. The latter required trips to Budapest, Port Harcourt, and the villages in Nigeria where my father lived, which also allowed me to immerse myself in the sights, smells, and sounds to depict them more authentically.

The chapters in this book are laid out in alternating points of view, addressing each parent's experiences separately. Although the book is set primarily in Africa and Europe, the themes of love, war, politics, poverty, immigration, and spirituality are relevant to readers of all backgrounds. We live in an increasingly interconnected world, requiring a greater understanding of diverse cultural experiences to get along. Intercultural conflicts have also dominated international news cycles around the world in recent years. The faces of violence and human suffering are diverse but universally tragic. Striking stories of love and compassion emerge from these traumas, revealing how global conflict can paradoxically highlight the unifying threads of shared humanity. The life of my parents spanned two continents and involved persevering through the political turmoil of the latter part of the twentieth century. It provides a small window into our culturally complex world, which will hopefully be an inspiration to readers.

I am grateful to everyone who gave up some of their time for this book. Thank you to my siblings, aunts, uncles, and cousins; to my parents' friends and acquaintances; and to others, who granted me interviews or shared materials pertaining to my mother or father. Many thanks to the beta-readers, editors, and book designers who were invaluable in transforming this book into its final form. I would like to acknowledge those who authored valuable literary works, which helped shape this book's rich narrative. Here, I highlight several books profiling Ijaw culture and history in remarkable detail by historian Ebiegberi Joe Alagoa, as well as Peter Bartók's inspiring book, *My Father*, an exemplary portrayal of a parent and Hungarian culture. I am also grateful to my younger sister Theresa for sharing her beautiful and touching essay, *Raised from a Distance*, which gives an intimate look into the personal effects of tragedy. Finally, thank you to Thelma for supporting me through the long, daunting writing process, and to my daughters, Caroline and Sophia, for motivating me to never give up on this project.

Daniel Tonye Mamah
St. Louis, Missouri.

CONTENTS

Chapter 1

MATTHEW

⁓

IN THE DAYS BEFORE THE coups, the universe opened its arms wide to Matthew.

It embraced the entire country, in a way, with a ravenous optimism like cool water beneath the hot Nigerian sun. Early in the 1960s, the country's hope for a fair government radiated from every home and marketplace, with no moment more intensely promising than the decade's first October. Shaking off the sticky humidity of September, the entire country slipped into a dream. They'd thrown off the shackles of colonialism and declared themselves officially independent from British rule. No longer under the thumb of Queen Elizabeth, Nigeria surged with opportunity.

But the sense of wide-open possibilities paled in comparison with Matthew's dreams for his future—or, perhaps just as accurately, his father's dreams for his future. From the time he'd been born, the family's only son, he'd felt an immense pressure to succeed. "Aim high and shoot high," his father always said, repeating the phrase until Matthew heard it in his dreams. A vote of genuine confidence, it sometimes felt like wind in the wings of a fish eagle, others, like a knee on his throat.

His most ardent supporter, his father looked at him and saw a future doctor, an engineer, a thriving professional. His father who woke them at five o'clock every morning. His father who always claimed the fish's flavorful head for his own. His father who called them all to prayer with the familiar cry of "*bo wa teke*." His father who sang gentle songs to ward away evil. "*Oru otu, paki mienyem, oro ifie faa nto*," he warbled, his voice a raspy baritone that was timid in tone but strong in purpose. "Juju people, you are doing, your time will soon be over."

His father, an ordained Anglican Priest, was at once unashamedly Christian and sentimental about his ancestors' disappearing religion. Matthew had learned the gospels alongside the stories of Woyengi, the Ijaw's creator and supreme deity. The benevolent "Great Mother," Woyengi defended the defenseless and punished the wicked. Dropped to earth in a bolt of lightning, she crafted dolls from the earth's abundant mud. She breathed life into them, giving them a choice of gender, occupation, or blessings, such as fertility, talent, or money. Depending on their life choices, some were sent down in a calm stream—others, in a torrent.

As he made his way down Port Harcourt's Nsukka Street, Matthew imagined the city as the torrent, his tiny village the calm stream. He marveled at the city's modernity. Rolling through the city on tarred roads—a phenomenon he'd very rarely seen—cars filed into a neat line, the sun gleaming off their shiny finishes.

He had never seen so many people wearing shoes! In Emelego, they'd walked barefoot to school, their feet growing calloused against the rough ground from their very first steps. Or, more frequently, people in his community traveled by river in canoes.

Here, people seemed to float above the city streets, packed together in a hustle and bustle he'd never experienced. Street hawkers shouted things as he passed, their voices startling him even as others around him seemed not to notice. And, unlike the mud-walled dwelling of his childhood, Port Harcourt homes boasted tile floors, slick and shiny beneath their dwellers' feet.

Before he came to the city, he'd understood their mud-walled house as quite fancy—the family had a parlor and a verandah, and the thatched-roof kitchen was attached to the home, unlike many of their neighbors'. He remembered running his hands over his father's grass mattress and along the iron bed frame. This, he had believed then, was the lap of luxury—a tangible goal he hoped to replicate when he someday became a father himself. Sure, he knew about rich people. Rich people lived in cities, success pouring over them by the bucketload. But they were far away, abstract, in a different universe. It wasn't so much that the city lifestyle was out of reach—although it was for most villagers—but that it was so different from his life that they almost seemed incomparable. Like a language that refused to be translated into his own. In Emelego, there weren't rich people and poor people; there were the villagers, and, in their wildest fantasies, there were others whose feet never touched the dusty earth.

Now those feet were his. He curled his toes against the steady beat that sent them slamming forward against the front of his shoes. Each motion grated with aggravating repetition as he traveled the farthest distance he'd ever walked in shoes. Thumping in his ears, his feet in his shoes, his shoes on his street, his street in his city, his city in his dreams.

But it wasn't a dream. This was his home now.

Port Harcourt buzzed and tittered with people. Birds chirped and lizards skittered about, just like at home, but here, the bustle of society obscured their little motions. Rushing to their next important event, none of the city people paid much attention to the birds or the lizards. He felt somewhere between an imposter and a welcomed guest. While none of the pedestrians paid much attention to him, he felt as though the city's own eyes were burning into the back of his neck. He held his head high above his lean frame, refusing to cower, even as he passed row after intimidating row of brick and stone and tile.

Before he knew it, he was standing in front of the house—his house. Stomach turning with excitement and anticipation—and, if he was honest, a touch of anxiety—he took a deep breath to calm his nerves and ran a hand over his close-cropped hair. He reassured himself by thinking of the house as cozy. A small house for so many people, it was really only the brick exterior that seemed different. And yet, the door in front of him felt intimidating as he raised his fist to knock.

"*Nua!*" The woman flung the door open before his knuckles could connect with the rough wood. Wearing a modest head tie, the woman flashed a toothy grin even brighter than the bold print that adorned her slim figure.

"*Yaa, okoido,*" Matthew stammered in response, holding himself in a semi-squat position, an Ijaw obeisance to elders.

"*Seiree.*" Get up.

"Ah, Okpoma!" a man's voice echoed in the background, addressing Matthew by his Ijaw name. "*Tubara?*"

"*Ebinimi,*" Matthew responded. I am good.

Mrs. Tudeigha wrapped her arms around him, like a cushion against the strange new world. Like Matthew, the Tudeighas were Ijaw and, thus, welcomed other Ijaws into their home. This was particularly true for those who lived independent from their families.

Independent.

The word had a strange ring to it. He'd always imagined himself venturing into the world, head held high, toward whatever adventure God had in store for him. As expected, nerves flooded his body, sending heat to his cheeks. But he hadn't anticipated the nostalgia, the yearning to be both here and there, in the city and in his village. The uncomfortable grating of past against future startled him, and he swallowed hard against the lump in his throat.

He felt something else, too, stranger than the nostalgia.

He searched his mind for what that feeling could be. Not determination, exactly, and certainly not calm.

He felt relieved.

After years of promises, he was here, living up to his father's expectations. Making him proud. It had been difficult to relax under the pressure he felt to succeed. And now he was here—ready to start his secondary schooling—his path clear and paved, fit for travel beneath the soles of the shoes that pinched his feet. His father would be proud.

But his father wasn't here. And, amid the city's buildings, with their plumb, smooth walls and sharp corners, neither was anything else that reminded him of his childhood. In a way, this mystical, inexplicable place reminded him of a glistening cube he'd once encountered. He'd been selling groundnuts when a friend convinced him to take a break and play in the common yard. As quickly as they'd begun, Matthew's feet slipped from under him. He launched forward onto the ground, knee first. Perhaps it was his own fault, he thought, for dallying when he should be focused on providing for the family. His knee screamed, but the pain was nothing compared to his bruised ego. Willing away the tears that threatened to fall with each aching step, he soldiered on, the regrettable moment of play hounding him like a rock in his gut.

"You alright, kid?"

He turned to see a man striding toward him, his skin as bright as the sun and hair different than that of anyone he knew. His knee throbbing, Matthew was slow, so the man soon caught up and fell into step next to him.

Matthew nodded a quick "yes, sir," but the man persisted, inviting the boy back to a nearby ship. As they walked, the man inquired about his injured knee. He responded honestly, a flush of heat in his cheeks, but the man didn't seem to think anything of it. Instead, in a thick British accent, he explained that he worked in the nearby oil field. He stopped short of buying any groundnuts, instead offering something magical—a shiny, translucent block that he fished out of a cup in his hands. Uncomfortably cold in his hand, the cube seemed to leach something wet onto his fingertips. The longer he held it, the wetter it got.

The man chuckled. Unsure of the block's purpose—or why his marvel had sparked the man's laughter—the boy hung his head.

The man reassured him. "Hold it on your knee," he said.

He did as he was told, and it did seem to ease the sting. Or maybe he just imagined that part. What he knew for sure was that the wet brick was the most amazing thing he'd ever seen. He had to show his mother. At his request for a new block—the first one had shrunk and shrunk until it vanished into liquid drips on the floor—the man laughed again. But he shrugged it off, eagerly pocketing the new wet brick. Knee pain forgotten, he raced home to show his mother, only to find the block missing and the lining of his pocket damp.

"*Wonasi aba rilo*!" his mother chided him in her native Ogbian, ignoring his explanations. You are lying!

He couldn't protest much—he wouldn't have believed it either.

Now, years later, something about Port Harcourt reminded him of that mystical, glistening cube. It was tangible but ephemeral like its beauty might slip through your fingers. With its palpable energy and shiny cars and promise—so much promise—the city felt almost like a lie. He wouldn't have believed it if someone had described it to him. With his own eyes, he could see the future his father had wanted for him. He'd never really grasped it before.

Until now.

The city's fantasy was dwarfed only by the anticipation of a new home, a new school, and a new life. Somehow it gave him the sense of being both grown up and very, very small. With a pang of remorse, he wished for one more night in his family home in Emelego, one more set of evening prayers with his father, one more word of comfort from his mother. But, like most teenagers, he buried his homesickness deep in his gut and focused his attention on the Tudeighas' beautiful home.

Matthew would soon come to call the Tudeighas "mama" and "papa," integrating into their home, crowded with the several other Ijaw youths they housed, as though he had always lived there. It was a joy to help them care for the house, like a rehearsal for his own future home. When the bushes that flanked the couple's home grew unruly, he volunteered to clear them with a machete. There was something so satisfying about tidying up the home's exterior, particularly when paired with his regular chore of cutting grass. The elongated, flexed rectangular blade would swish through the thick grass until it revealed the neat perfection he loved.

The swish of the cutlass mimicked his other favorite chore: sweeping the floor. He found the repeated motions of the broom soothing. Lashed together with jute cording, the long bristles scraped the floor with a gentle, rhythmic swoosh.

It was just one of the sounds he'd come to associate with the city.

Beyond the bustle of the home and busy streets, music seemed to radiate from Port Harcourt's soul. Matthew had hardly heard highlife music before, but suddenly it was everywhere. His favorite songs began with the rhythmic brr-chuk-chuk-tika-chuk of a drum kit. A splash of cymbals followed, proceeded by the rich harmony of horns. As the trumpets blared, in that brash sound immediately recognizable as jazz, the rhythm section picked up the groove of traditional African drum patterns. The tinny guitar riffs danced beneath it all, the rich, vibrant layers seeping into listeners' bones, calling them to dance along with the bandleaders.

The energizing accompaniment followed him to Niger Grammar School. Flanked by long rows of tall palm trees, the campus took his breath away. Only a few years old, the buildings that housed classrooms and dormitories spread out, vast, across the sprawling campus. Their bold presence was second only to that of the school's founding principal. Chief Nicholas Frank-Opigo was the very definition of "aim high and shoot high," an Ijaw man whose confident stare seemed to punctuate his brilliance and stature in the community. The students didn't dare disappoint him—Matthew included—lest they fall short of the school's near-perfect record of successfully completing the graduation certification examination.

An excellent student, Matthew was hungry for success—and not only in his studies. Something about his upbringing combined with the optimism of the time sparked a deep sense of competition in him. He often played Monopoly with friends—all clad in white shirts and tan pants—before moving on to chess, the game that would become his lifelong love. With its elegant politics—mimicking colonial battles over lands and their people—chess fit neatly beside his fascination with current events.

In the years before the Prime Minister fell, Matthew had followed Nigerian news closely. The country had been in transition for two years before he arrived in that awe-inspiring city. The next year, there was a new president. Prime Minister Balewa was still a powerful force in the government, but now they were a republic. President Azikiwe—Zik, as he preferred to be called—was Igbo like the revolutionaries who would eventually remove him from office, but by the time he became president, he'd lived all over the nation. Fluent in Yoruba as well as Igbo and Hausa, Zik had traveled to the United States of America for his education, and he brought an inspiring message of unity to the Nigerian government. He was a trained journalist and the founder of Matthew's preferred newspaper, the *West African Pilot*. After being tried for sedition for an article he'd written, Zik had been released on appeal and used his new lease on life to work toward the social change the country needed. This was a man who had stood on principle, even in the face of punishment. An independent thinker determined to make his nation better, Matthew recognized in him a deep sense of fairness similar to his own.

He was an inspiration, but for young Matthew, political aspirations were impractical at best. Instead, he'd set his eye on the field of Chemical Engineering. The degree would make him competitive for jobs with Shell, one of the few companies in Nigeria that promised good wages. Employment at Shell, he'd learned, included perks like housing, travel, and promotion from within. Perhaps he was a bit biased. After all, the man with the mystical cube had worked for Shell, and the experience imprinted on him a connection between success and oil. It was a big business, and big business meant a big life. Oil could buy you a brick house. It could buy you a metal bedframe. It could buy you delicious food to eat and journeys to fascinating places. This, unlike political ambitions, was a way to raise himself up—to become the son his father dreamed of.

And then, one day early in 1966, Matthew turned on the radio. "Balewa has been killed! The Prime Minister is dead!" the announcer shouted, a flood of emotion distorting his voice. "There's been a coup d'etat!" Nigerians were still holding fast to the optimism of the early 1960s, but in the years since he'd arrived at Port Harcourt, things had been going steadily downhill. Revolutionary violence plagued the nation's cities. People were afraid to walk in the streets. But, as cautious as ordinary people were, everyone assumed the Prime Minister was safe. Now, Balewa had been assassinated. Zik, overthrown.

Only days before, the *West African Pilot* had run a celebratory story. Lagos played host to the Commonwealth Conference, the first gathering of the leaders of the commonwealths to take place outside England. Rebellion had arisen in Rhodesia over minority rule, and an impressive slate of governors came together to brainstorm non-violent solutions for the uprising. The newspaper's cloudy image camouflaged the deep lines that framed Balewa's mouth like parentheses. And yet his expressive face shone through the inky pixels. Balewa's tall, white kufi cap raised his stature, making him inches taller than the entourage of British rulers. An imperfect leader, he'd nonetheless held the hope of Nigeria on his shoulders.

Now, just two days after the conference, he was dead.

His body was found along the side of a dirt road, half a decade of optimism crumpled into the sickening lump of a discarded corpse. Balewa's death was just the first of many. The revolutionaries behind the coup attacked multiple cities in northern and western Nigeria, leaving an opening for the army's commanding officer to rise to power. From the Igbo south—like the revolutionaries—General Johnson Aguiyi-Ironsi had taken over the nascent democracy.

Just six years after declaring its independence from Great Britain, Nigeria was a military state. For many, Balewa's death had robbed the country of its optimism.

But not for Matthew. For Matthew, this new political world was a calling.

Chapter 2

JUDIT

⁓

WOMEN IN CLOCHES AND MEN in trilby hats bustled down Bocskai Road, making their way to work or social gatherings. The street was replete with gray cobblestones and trees that stretched over the sidewalk, and there had been increasing car and bus traffic over the past several years. The occasional bicycle zipped through the pedestrians.

A horse-drawn wagon made its way down the street, the driver's head tilted as he yelled out "*Jeges*," the Hungarian word for iceman. "Jeges! Jeges!" he repeated as he rode by.

The wagon came to a stop as women and children made their way out with buckets to collect the ice. The iceman raised his pick, cleaving the ice into clean blocks for each family to take home to their icebox for food storage.

If anyone walking along the sidewalk that day had looked up, they would have spotted a little girl gazing down from her family's second-floor apartment at the corner of Zsombolyai Street. The squared-off building was tidy and sharp except for the curved balconies on the building's corner, stacked up, one floor on top of another, as the apartments reached into the sky. The balcony would be an inviting place to watch the street from, but her mother had asked that Judit stay inside, gazing out only through the window.

The city was always so busy. Judit found it remarkable how people always seemed to be moving. Whether summer heat radiated from the sidewalks or a slick layer of ice caked the streets, people always had somewhere to be. Sometimes the energy felt uplifting and exciting—optimistic. Other times, she wondered if something darker lurked below.

Soon after the war, the Soviets had begun to stretch their reach into nearby countries, and they formally controlled Hungary by 1949. The situation left many children thin and undernourished and forced adults to produce iron and steel for Russian consumption. For children like Judit, Communism was mostly about rules. Courses they had to take—Russian and Marxist Philosophy—as well as things they couldn't say or do.

Twelve-year-old Judit didn't remember another Hungary. But the old country—the country before the Soviets—stretched itself out before her in her dreams. A mix of her mother's stories and Judit's own fanciful daydreaming, this world was a fantasy of the past—a distorted echo of the family's past prosperity. In it, her home overlooked cascading hills of green and gold. The harvest promised to keep them well-fed and, maybe, earn enough at the market for a new dress of crisp, white linen. In this dream world, her mother stuffed cabbage leaves full of beef. She stewed chicken thighs in a rich paprika sour cream sauce. She gently lowered platters of lamb and asparagus onto a smooth, fresh tablecloth. Dogs and horses and chickens scattered about the vast landscape, and the sun set over an idyllic creek as if lowering its glaring face to listen quietly to the water's gentle babble and the frog's rhythmic croaks.

The family shared these stories, memories inflated by longing, as they themselves grew thinner and wearier. Back then, Judit knew, the country wasn't perfect—at least not in the way she imagined it. But it had, at least, been fair. This new world of never enough, of political strife, of the constant weight of Soviet influence, somehow mixed with an unlikely optimism for change—now, this was the life she knew.

As the youngest of five children, Judit was often pampered. After they'd moved to the city—before the most serious consequences of Russian control had rained down onto the country—she'd often been showered with small luxuries. Her siblings had created a toy zoo for her years earlier, painstakingly cutting animal shapes from wood with a fretsaw. They'd decorated them with brightly colored paint and assembled them into a menagerie that made her eyes shine with delight.

The next year, she'd even hosted a birthday party, an increasingly rare event in communist Hungary. Her mother prepared foamy chocolate milk and kalács. While the braided sweet bread wasn't a birthday cake—a lavish treat in the face of massive inflation and general economic devastation—the children didn't mind. They greedily devoured big, doughy bites, licking their sugary fingers clean. These little pleasures delighted Judit, a whimsical child who tended toward daydreaming.

Her mother frequently scolded her flightiness, perhaps out of fear as much as frustration, particularly after the incident with the horse. While visiting her father's friend as a very young girl, Judit had set out to explore. The man's horses were quite old and gentle, and he assured her mother that the little girl would be safe. Fascinated, she'd walked around the horse. Her favorite doll dangling at her side, she admired the animal's smooth, brown coat and black tail from all angles. She'd talked with the horse, taking care, as she had been instructed, to keep her fingers back.

But no one had told her to avoid the horse's rear. As she ran gleefully behind the animal, she squealed, prompting it to strike out. Its back hoof connected with Judit's face, blocked only by the prized doll. Face drenched in blood, she lay on the ground screaming until her father could scoop her up and race her to the house, the shattered toy abandoned in the pasture.

In the end, the injury was relatively minor. The doctor stitched closed the three-centimeter gash above her right eyebrow. Had she been only a centimeter taller, he quipped, she might have lost her right eye.

The memory had stuck with her—shaped as much by others' recollections as her own—but not as much as it had haunted her parents. Her father blamed himself for the accident. An experienced farmer, he was no stranger to livestock; it simply hadn't occurred to him that she would run behind the horse. The memory stoked her mother's wariness, and she watched her youngest child with a careful eye. In truth, her mother probably would have babied her anyway, even if not for the horse.

Judit always looked young to her family, with her round face, big brown eyes, and thick blond hair that had only just begun to darken. But, as all children do, she hated being treated like a baby. She knew who she was: a girl deeply concerned with fairness, fighting for the oppressed, and standing up for what was right. Scatter-brained as she was, she had an unwavering moral compass, preferring to stand up for the underdog, even when the decision was unpopular.

Her steadfastness grated awkwardly against her country's rising instability. As Hungarians struggled against the chains of Communism, the rights of the people became unpredictable. Russian control ruined the Hungarian economy before their eyes, and yet they were expected to pledge allegiance to this corrupt, exploitative government. Soon, revolutionaries emerged where ordinary people had once stood. Beneath the family's western Budapest apartment, traffic bustled, sending the energy of the street below wafting up to their apartment windows.

That energy changed in an instant when, in late October 1956, revolution erupted.

Where Budapesters had once drug their feet along Bocskai road, their footfalls like the ticking of cogs in a Soviet machine, the street buzzed with optimism. Hungarians donned oblong bunches of ribbon on their caps and coats. A colorful explosion that echoed the Hungarian flag, the red, white, and green cockades shouted with national pride. Once pressed to near-bursting beneath the heels of Soviet boots, the forbidden nationalist sentiment suddenly exploded.

The entire character of the city changed overnight. Refrains of "*Éljen a Magyar Szabadság*," rang out, a melodic call for the eternal persistence of the free Hungarian spirit. Judit often heard enthusiastic chanting from the streets, and, on the radio, announcers swore their allegiance to their country, occasionally playing the national anthem.

The spirit in the air was intoxicating.

And then it came into their apartment.

She hadn't been surprised to hear her brother-in-law, Béla Hajtman, speak with such passion about the revolution. An outspoken yet stoic young man, Bori's husband seemed transformed by the city's energy, challenging the family with fiery refutations if anyone even so much as questioned the uprising. Judit listened with a secretive curiosity. The whole idea of revolution seemed illicit—dangerous—but he spoke seductively, with a fervor she'd only heard in folk tales.

Her sister was more concerned. Desperate to keep Hajtman safe, Bori was determined to tamp down her husband's revolutionary spirit. When they fought, their voices hushed in the cramped space they borrowed from her parents, Judit tried not to listen, but the moment's drama spoke to her flair for fantasy. As the youngest, she was often overlooked in the apartment, her adult siblings and parents shuffling about their business, so she used her invisibility to quietly bask in the drama of the moment. She longed to be invited into her older siblings' worlds, to live the life she imagined as glamorous and romantic. Instead, she was instructed to be quiet, so as not to wake her baby niece.

That was certainly the case the day Bori and Hajtman left baby Tonó in her crib—a rickety old thing that was tucked away in a back bedroom of the apartment—and left for the theater. The apartment was small but kept clean and cared for with white curtains and fresh flowers on the table when they were in season. Some of the furniture was adorned with brightly-colored Hungarian motifs painted by Judit's father.

Careful to walk lightly, Judit tightened her bow—she always wore a bow in her hair—and wandered into the kitchen where her mother, with her hair tied out of her face, stood over the stove, stirring the family's meager dinner. The silence of the apartment immediately gave way to the rising whirr of the air-raid siren. Her instinct had once been to drop to her knees. They often practiced air-raid exercises in school, tucking themselves under their desks, fingers interlaced behind their skulls, as they pressed their foreheads to the floor.

But, in the days since the revolution, the sirens had increased in frequency and, thus, decreased in effectiveness as her family and others had grown used to that once-ominous tone.

Berci rose from his seat in the tiny kitchen, moving toward the apartment window with curiosity, but her mother remained at the stove. Judit stared, taking in the scene.

"Now, Jutka, let's go!"

She jumped at the sudden sound of her father's voice, despite his gentle use of her pet name. With a tight smile, he patted her shoulder, nudging her toward the stairwell that led to the building's basement. She knew better than to grumble. While her father was always kind—and quite nurturing by the standards of the time—he was not prone to negotiating with his adolescent children. Judit dawdled after her sister and father, as they made their way downstairs, glancing back at her brother with a mixture of longing and deeply-concealed fear as he perched in the window that overlooked the busy street below.

As they closed the apartment door and filtered into the slowly spiraling stairwell, Judit thought she heard her brother shout in a panicked tone she hadn't heard before. She tried to pause for just a moment on the tiled landing, but her sister kept walking. She'd been just a step ahead of Judit, her blond hair bobbing with each step, but was she walking faster now? Or did the space simply feel more urgent as neighbors flooded the narrow shaft? She set her face to stone and did as she was told, following closely behind Potyi but careful not to push.

The hoard of people filed into the basement, and the utility door propped from hand to hand as it welcomed each new resident. Blended with the wailing sirens, the chatter grew louder, comforting white noise that softened the sour feeling in Judit's gut.

Tearing through the lackadaisical chatter, the loud steady puck-a-puck-a-puck of machine-gun fire was a flourishing prelude to the ear-splitting whoosh of the explosion.

Suddenly, the basement erupted in chaos. Neighbors had been casually filtering down to the basement. Now, they clamored for safety. The conversational tone shifted from a friendly mix of mild concern and cynicism to something that sounded, at least to her ears, like panic. With her eyes glued to the door, she willed her mother to appear. Her brother had been sitting in the window over Zsombolyai street when last she saw him, and the baby sleeping soundly in her crib. A force of heat and pressure rushed from her chest to her throat. Her head rang with a strange, metallic vibration.

It wasn't until she felt her sister's hand on her arm that she realized she'd been holding her breath. Around her, the flurry of activity felt both too fast and too slow. She scanned each face, searching for her mother's thin lips and bright blue eyes. She clung to her sister, as the screams of her neighbors—much too loud for the small space—dissipated to a dull hum. She turned to her father, forgetting for one blessed moment that he'd gone back upstairs. Her stomach flipped as she realized what that meant. Together with her sister, she would simply have to sit and wait in the vain hope that everything was okay.

She bowed her head and whispered a soft prayer. When she looked up, her mother appeared across the room. Clothes rumpled and hair flaked with debris, tears streaked her face. But she was whole. Baby Tonó cradled in her arms, her mother made her way to the family, Berci following close behind.

Her mother had wanted to keep the sauce warm, she'd told them, a tinge of regret in her voice. Even when Berci had spotted commotion outside, she'd assumed it was a false alarm. He'd moved from the window after he'd spotted the unusual progression of traffic. In front of their building, across the road, he'd first seen soldiers.

Then Humvees.

Then Tanks.

As Berci described the scene, Judit hung on his every word. "The Ruskies are coming!" he'd shouted. Still, their mother hadn't believed him—she hadn't wanted to believe that the joy and hope the revolution had brought to the streets was being stamped out by Stalin's angry boots.

When the terrible sounds had begun—in the chaos, they weren't yet sure what they'd heard—they'd all hit the floor. They'd waited for the sounds to stop, then scurried to the basement.

Judit wasn't sure how long the family stayed in the cocoon of the shelter. Time had been derailed from its track as she waited, both eager for the comfort of her home and too terrified to go upstairs. But eventually, neighbors began to filter out of the basement, and her family followed suit.

What awaited the family was more horrifying than anything they could have imagined. The living room was unrecognizable, shards of glass scattered across the floor, shrapnel and building debris layered across everything. Even the little food the family had—food that their mother had stayed to tend—had been scattered with bits of glass and dust, remnants of the plaster that once formed the exterior wall that faced Bocskai Road.

Later, they would learn that the blast had originated from a tank at the opposite end of the road, next to a government office. It had rotated as it fired, discharging projectiles into a broad swath of apartment complexes. Separated from the tank by a massive column of iron and concrete, the family's home had escaped the worst damage, a strange thought when they looked around the devastated room. But, compared to other apartments, their home had been spared. The Fábián's apartment next door bore a fifteen-square-meter hole.

The vision of her mother standing over the stove—just as she had been when Judit went downstairs—lingered in the back of her mind for a long time. Crying as she fished a fragment of glass from the rich sauce, her mother suddenly looked older, frail.

The street outside the apartment was full of sorrow. The wails of mourners replaced the spirited songs and chants, which suddenly seemed like a distant memory. The flags, with the Soviet seal cut from their centers, were pulled down, replaced with the same flags that had always flown there—their colors bold and fabric new. Only the people who walked beneath them appeared beaten down. A few brave fighters lingered, smearing business windows with "*Ruszkik haza!*" Ruskies go home. Nonetheless, within the week, the revolution was pronounced dead. The two-week effort prompted Russia to strengthen its already iron grip. With 2,500 Hungarians dead, the Soviets took their seven-hundred deaths in stride, doubling down to arrest tens of thousands of supposed revolutionaries. They executed hundreds.

There was something deeply unsettling about the way the revolution had ended. Judit despised Soviet control, from the hunger that made her thin to the mandated Russian classes. Enthralled by the idea of fighting back, she had spun a fantasy of political overthrow.

Now, she saw what revolution was. It was death. It was destruction. It was a horrible action that hoped, but failed, to replace another horrible action, both of which ushered in unimaginable, inhumane conditions.

The family launched into a cooperative effort to salvage what they could, banding together with water pails and mops and brushes and trash bins. Her parents kept their spirits up, but their grins looked too big, their chins held too high. Partitioned from the rest of the apartment, the devastated living room sat dormant until they could properly address it. It would take money they didn't have to arrange for professional repairs.

Eventually, the apartment resembled what it had before the blast, but the country never did, at least not for a long, long time. With his deeply cleft chin and thick, rubbery skin, the Hungarian Premier, János Kádár might have offered some hope. He announced amnesty and echoed the major demands of the revolutionaries.

But, still, tanks and guns lingered in the streets of Budapest.

Within two years, former revolutionary Imre Nagy had been executed, the principles he'd died for swept away, replaced once again by the slow, suffering torment of the Soviets.

As hopeless as Hungarians had felt before the revolution, it was nothing compared to how they felt after. Spirits quashed and leaders murdered, now they had no options. Two hundred thousand of their people fled the country, and Budapest bore the marks of tanks and guns for years to come, a sickly, blackened reminder of their powerlessness.

All that was left was to live with the fallout.

Chapter 3

A LAND OF RIVERS

THE CHAPEL STRETCHED OUT LONG and narrow before Matthew, his schoolmates' voices dancing around him.

"Leaning on the everlasting arms," they sang, the happy tune delirious in his ear. Lilting and joyful, as is the Methodists' way, the sweet melody threatened to rot one's teeth.

He checked his watch.

To his right, a student caught the spirit. He swayed with the beat, brushing against Matthew's elbow with each upbeat. Matthew took a small step to his left and scratched an itch on his shoulder.

"Leaning, leaning."

Standing wedged between long wooden pews reminded him of his childhood and pulled him back to his father's church in Emelego. The church had been the nicest building in that small town. Since then, his father had been posted to another town, another parish.

"Safe and secure from all alarms," the young man next to him sang along. Matthew sighed. He couldn't understand the school's

requirement to go to chapel so often, just to stand here and sing these silly hymns. The music had torn him away from other things he could be doing: reading, relaxing, or preparing for his chemistry test—at best, an unnecessary distraction; at worst, a waste of time.

"Leaning, leaning..."

He checked his watch again. After a quick reconnaissance, he pulled the morning's *West African Pilot* from the leather bag that carried his books. He glanced around again and opened it, holding it just below the pew in front of him. No one had seen him, as far as he could tell.

The *Pilot* had been following the country's main story closely. Just a few days prior, General Yakubu Gowon, Nigeria's President, had broken the country's four regions into twelve independent states, one among them a shining beacon of hope—Rivers State.

Rivers State.

The words tasted like a promise. Badly neglected first by the British, and now by the new military government, the Ijaws—his people—had little political representation under the previous system. Their oil-rich land remained poor and underdeveloped even as others benefitted from its natural resources.

The state system, Matthew hoped, would be different. At the thought, excitement rattled through him. He thought, first, of his mother. Burned into his mind was the image of his mother climbing into her canoe and paddling away. He and his older sister Comfort, then small children, watched her shrink into the distance, waving as her shape faded in the morning mist.

Once, he'd asked to go along with her.

"No," she'd said. "I have to go home to farm. But I'll come back."

He'd waved and obediently remained with Comfort.

Comfort watched him during the day, prepared his meals, swept the floors, scrubbed the pot, and gathered firewood. Like their mother, she worked from very early in the morning until very late at night.

Neither had much time to rest.

A pointless waste of human potential, the grinding work expectations of poverty bludgeoned his family's spirits while their people's land brought riches to men in the cities.

As a child, he hadn't understood.

But he did now.

He glanced down at the newspaper carefully nestled in his hand and furrowed his brow at the headline.

"Republic of Biafra is Born," it read.

"Biafra," he repeated aloud, puzzled by the unfamiliar word.

Suddenly, the singing stopped and quiet fell over the chapel. His heart raced for a moment as he glanced around, dropping the newspaper to his side. At the first chattering voices, he realized the students had been dismissed. Relieved, he tucked the paper into his bag.

During chapel, he'd been anxious to leave. He needed to get to mathematics class—one of his favorites. But the newsprint screamed at him from his schoolbag. Biafra. Stepping to the side once out of the chapel doors, he paused to place his bag on the ground and retrieve the paper.

He tried to make sense of the story. Colonel Chukwuemeka Ojukwu, the governor of the eastern region before the twelve-state reorganization, had made the declaration. It grew more serious with each printed line.

Violence had spread across Nigeria while Matthew and his friend Eze had been doing their A-level studies at Methodist.

While they had been focused on the university prep courses in math and chemistry, the country became more and more unstable. After the coup that killed Balewa, anti-Igbo sentiment had exploded, heating tribal tensions to their boiling point. Particularly in the North, Igbo populations were being murdered or chased out.

Personally, Matthew didn't worry about becoming a target. With his very dark skin and short stature, he didn't look particularly Igbo. His last name, Mamah, didn't have a clear tribal association, making his background hard to place. Also, like other students, he mostly stayed on campus where people expected to encounter classmates from different ethnic groups.

Although the tribal violence had never threatened his own life, he'd nonetheless felt the change in his country. People shuddered through chance interactions and averted their eyes from every narrowed gaze or assertive approach.

"Where are you from?" their suspicious faces screamed. "Are you my broda?"

It was unsustainable, Matthew agreed, scanning the article. But the twelve-state system had promised to remedy the problem. So, he wondered, why now? Why secede just when the promise of a Rivers State—of the other states, too—opened possibilities across the country?

Matthew stared at the story, his mind racing from explanation to argument, trying to connect the dots on a puzzle he couldn't quite make out.

"Hey," a voice behind him said.

Matthew looked up, startled to see Eze standing there. "Let's go." He tilted his head toward the classroom building, "Class."

"I'm coming." Matthew shoved the newspaper into his bag and

headed toward mathematics class, his mind still turning over the news story.

He wasn't sure what it meant, but it felt strange and vaguely ominous, particularly in contrast to the lightness he'd felt at the announcement of a Rivers State a few days prior. Still, he tried to reassure himself.

Whatever the declaration of Biafra meant, he hoped everything would be fine.

He should have known better.

In his short time in Uzuakoli, Nigeria had flipped upside down. The coup that killed Balewa in 1966 had replaced him with General Aguiyi-Ironsi. Within a month of Aguiyi-Ironsi's rule, Isaac Boro, a man not much older than Matthew, had declared independence for the Niger Delta, which encompassed all the Ijaw-speaking regions in southern Nigeria. Boro had organized a volunteer service and, for twelve days, Matthew had called the Niger Delta Republic home.

Those twelve days had tasted of promise.

Within a year, both Aguiyi-Ironsi and Boro were dead. Just thirty-five years old, General Yakubu Gowon had taken the helm of the Nigerian government. With each power shift, the country tilted further off its axis, spilling blood and hope as it spun out of control.

Matthew and his schoolmates had moved to Uzuakoli when it was part of the eastern region. In 1967, Gowon carved the region into states—each of which would have less influence than the original regions. Angry at his dwindling power, the governor of the region, Colonel Ojukwu, declared secession.

Reading the newspaper during chapel, Matthew learned that he and most of his schoolmates were citizens of Biafra.

Almost as quickly, Nigeria plunged into civil war.

Gradually but with horrifying certainty, the Igbo killings that had grown from the coups the year before morphed into an even crueler kind of murder. They'd been followed by reciprocal killings of Northerners. The 1966 anti-Igbo pogrom led to thousands—perhaps even tens of thousands—of Igbos killed and a million Igbos fleeing back to the East, primarily from the North. In response, some Northerners were massacred in Port Harcourt and other eastern regions.

Matthew's heart ached for the people of his country. He was also frustrated. He knew he shouldn't focus on his own losses, particularly when they paled in comparison to the suffering he read about in the paper. Still, when he thought of how the war had interrupted his plans, rage burned in his gut, followed quickly by anxiety. His meticulous plans had been dashed to the ground along with the nation.

For some time, Methodist College seemed fine.

Then things started to fall apart.

He started seeing soldiers in fatigues roaming the streets with trucks and guns. Soon after, the school itself went downhill as well. Some days classes were canceled. Students trickled out, returning home to their villages. With Uzuakoli right in the center of Biafra, the writing was on the wall.

His friend Eze knew someone who attended Hussey College, another A-level program in Warri. His friend had heard that things were better there. It was a bit more geographically removed from the real military action.

It could be a welcome alternative to Uzuakoli, where he'd seen military presence grow seemingly every day with his own two eyes.

The whole situation turned his stomach. As though his emotions had grown too large for his skin, he found that he couldn't sit still, the tense uncertainty around him seeping through his body and propelling him into restlessness.

Nothing felt familiar. Not the chapel. Not the campus. Not even—and perhaps especially not—Nigeria.

So by the time the college told students to return home, most had already planned to leave. Matthew had already packed his few belongings for travel to his father's village. Before he'd left home for Port Harcourt all those years ago, he'd traveled only by foot and canoe. Those first steps on the streets of the city had felt foreign but flooded with possibility.

Now, again, his steps felt like the actions of a body that was not his own. As he took one step after another toward the motor park at the edge of Uzuakoli, where he would set out to leave the town, the movement reeked not of promise, but of necessity.

Suddenly, a woman screamed.

Then, the sound of shots, *pop pop*.

His breath caught in his throat. He swiveled, scanning. His heart raced.

Nothing. Perhaps it had been a car backfiring. No one appeared to be hurt.

He'd lived the pattern many times over the past months—as soon as he calmed his nerves, it seemed, he would hear another sound. Or maybe he just thought he did. A gasp. Raised voices. He could find no other comfort than the knowledge that he would soon be back among the people he knew—his people.

That instinct drove him.

As he made his way through the streets, his route was lined with people. They walked with anxious purpose, many carrying belongings on their heads and babies on their backs. Some criss-crossed his path, some surpassed him as they rushed, like him, toward the fastest means of transportation to the city—the motor park.

The scene made the past month's chaos seem relatively calm. The motor park's energy was always somewhat frenetic, with drivers shouting their fares and riders scrambling to pay them. But this was like nothing he'd seen before. Around him, people brushed past one another, walking briskly as minibus and car operators yelled prices and routes over the noise.

"Aba! Port Harcourt!" yelled a man in a yellow tunic.

"One seat!" The voice came from behind Matthew, and he jumped. He turned to see a man with hollowed-out cheeks. "Warri!" He looked over in Matthew's direction and repeated, "Warri?!"

Matthew shook his head. "No," he said, pushing forward, away from the man toward a cluster of minibuses. As he looked, one bus pulled away. Another closed its door.

He scanned the park. A car horn blared and he turned to see a sedan pushing slowly forward through the crowd, people scattering as the driver moved too quickly through the crowded park.

"Port Harcourt?!" Matthew yelled.

A man in his left periphery waved his arms. "Port Harcourt! *Ngwa*, come!"

Behind the man was a bright yellow minibus. Through the windows, he saw too many people for the size of the vehicle. Men leaned out the windows, women behind them fanning themselves.

The man turned back to him, grabbing the money from his hand. "Close!" he said, indicating the door of the minibus.

He squeezed onboard. It was cramped, overflowing with people. Mothers with babies. Small children. Older teenagers, like himself, perhaps students. An elderly man.

Yet, as the bus inched through the crowded park, he felt a sense of relief. He had made it this far. Soon, he thought, they would merge onto the open road, quieter and more peaceful than the city.

But the chaos had seeped into the countryside. As they went south toward Port Harcourt, the roads were lined with people. They walked in a long trail along the edge of the road, like ants carrying the weight of their belongings—and the weight of their fear.

Occasionally the line of people would veer to the side, avoiding a car pulled over on the side of the road. Military men shouted into the cars. "Who are you?! Where are you from?!"

He'd heard these interrogations before. Searching for saboteurs, military men would ruthlessly question people for no reason he could decipher. He kept his face forward, keeping his expression purposefully calm.

All was fine, he reassured himself—fully aware of the lie.

No reason to be nervous.

He was not, after all, doing anything wrong.

But the thought nagged at him that neither had those who were being stopped.

Out of the corner of his eye, he saw two people. They lay face down along the side of the road. Two soldiers circled the car.

They've just been ordered to lay there, he told himself. Their car has been commandeered. They would be fine.

He repeated these reassurances to himself until they sounded like a hymn. However hollow, the patter of positivity was all he had.

For a time, the minibus's path seemed to clear of other vehicles. The sun set, its bright red glow silhouetting the people who continued to march along the road. Darker and darker it grew, until he felt the bus soldiering on into the pitch black of the night toward Port Harcourt.

He hadn't realized how much time he'd lost, traveling from the school to the motor park, waiting for an open space on a vehicle, boarding, and creeping out of the city amid the mass of people.

Finally, he began to see scattered lights, as the city came into view. He'd always loved Port Harcourt. Despite realizing that nowhere is really safe, he couldn't help but feel comforted.

He gazed out the front window of the minibus.

Suddenly, everything went bright. Blinding. The passengers lit up in a piercing glow. A woman gasped. A baby cried. Matthew's heart leapt into his throat.

The bus lurched to a stop.

"Everybody, come out!" a man shouted. "Come out! Are you not hearing?!"

The last one to board, Matthew was the first to exit.

"Hands on your head! Hands on your head!" the voice continued. Fast. Loud. Menacing.

He did as he was told, his eyes finally adjusting to the light. As he became aware of his surroundings, he identified its source. A military vehicle.

"You! Where are you coming from?!" yelled a man in a green khaki uniform and a Panama hat. A gun was slung across his torso.

A few paces in front of Matthew, a man sputtered, "Uzuakoli."

"Are you from Rivers State?!" another soldier yelled, addressing a family to Matthew's left.

"Yes," the father said.

The man's wife looked aghast. Matthew kept his face forward.

All around him, the interrogations continued. "Are you working with the Nigerian government?!" "Who are you?!" "Why are you going to Port Harcourt?!"

When it was Matthew's turn, the answer was simple.

"What tribe are you from?!"

"Ijaw."

The soldier paused for a moment, looking Matthew up and down. Without a word, he moved on. The threat was gone, or, at least, he hoped it was. But his body could not seem to settle. When they were finally allowed to reboard the minibus and make their way into Port Harcourt, his hands shook.

As though drawn by an invisible string, Matthew walked mechanically through the city to the Tudeighas. Early the next morning he headed west to his father's new post in the waterside town of Ekowe.

———

He met his father just outside the small house where he lived alone. After some difficulties in their relationship, his mother and father had parted ways, an occurrence Matthew knew little about, other than that the experience had lingered as a wound on his father's heart.

"Nua, Papa!" he exclaimed as he saw his father.

"Okpoma!" his father responded excitedly, a white clergy collar prominent over his black short-sleeved shirt. "Nua! Nua o!" he continued, as he wrapped his arms around his son.

Matthew thought he might collapse with the relief, his father's pocked face and soft voice like a salve. As a child, he'd experienced his father's care as a shield, as many children do. But he had not expected it to flood him with such relief as a young man.

He felt as though he was a child again, his father's embrace a respite from the landscape he'd just traversed.

His father stepped back from him. "Gracious God," he said, and Matthew bowed his head instinctively. "We are so grateful that you have provided safe passage." His father's voice wavered. "Merciful, powerful Father. Thank you."

For the next several months, Matthew leaned into the comfort of the familiar. At times, he traveled by canoe between Ekowe and Ogbia to visit his mother. Mostly, he laid low. With uncertainty hanging in the air like a dark, toxic cloud, it was difficult to imagine wandering too far from the villages he knew.

As those months wore on, the same sense of threat he'd felt in the cities crept into the villages in the form of stories. The villages were, in a way, sheltered from the war, but the war's stories still crept across the region like the rivers that lined the lands. People were afraid of the seemingly random military violence. People were afraid of conscription—men around Matthew's age being forced to join the military. Most of all, people were afraid of what the future would hold.

Villagers spread stories, as people do. And, as people do, they slowly acclimated to this new world of instability and threat.

Matthew's own urge to bunker down began to erode, and as it did, it collided with a growing sense of frustration. He'd traveled to Uzuakoli to move his life forward. Now, here he was. Back where he'd started.

Eventually, he sat with his father and shared the plans that had grown more and more concrete in his mind.

"I want to go to Warri. I cannot sit and wait for the danger to be gone before I finish my education." He leaned forward, speaking with a passion that belied his inner conflict. He believed this was the right choice, but he knew the path was far from safe.

His father was quiet, his head nodding imperceptibly as he became lost in thought. In the silence of the room, Matthew sensed a new type of closeness with his father. His father had dreamed of his success—he'd pushed him since he was just a child, urging him to pursue education and growth. Still, he'd felt hesitant to raise the issue with his father, perhaps because the same fear that twisted in his gut was etched across his father's face.

They sat in the quiet darkness for some time.

Then, his father looked into his eyes with the faithful resolve he'd often seen in the older man's eyes—a look that communicated determination and faith. "Bo wa teke," his father said.

The familiar words comforted Matthew as much as his embrace.

The next day, his father seemed resolved. "God's gifts always arrive on time," he told his son.

While confused at first by his father's cryptic language, Matthew soon understood. Ever since he'd returned home, he'd noticed his father looked somehow less tired, less slouched than he remembered.

His father had devoted his life to spreading Christianity across the Riverine region, work that required him to traverse the rivers that branched out like veins across the landscape. Since many villages lacked priests, he would go to lead worship and perform other duties. Like most people who traveled between villages in the area, he'd long done so with a paddle canoe. It was hard and exhausting work.

Now, a grin spread over his father's face as he motioned for Matthew to follow him, "Come and see!"

It was a motorized canoe—although it now looked more like a boat—with an Archimedes-brand engine, a green surface, and pillars that held up a roof reading, *Ayeba Ebi Egberi*," an Ijaw phrase meaning "God's Good News." Matthew could see immediately how it had changed his father's traveling work and could easily imagine his father standing on the deck, addressing gathered congregants on the bank, eagerly taking in God's good news.

His father was a soft-spoken man who was beloved in his role. In fact, Matthew knew of at least one instance of a congregant telling him to speak up.

A woman had stopped him and remarked, "Your preachings are very good, but you should speak out *nah*, nobody go hear you!"

His father had straightened his back, standing tall in his white preacher's robe, and tightened the black string belt. Then he'd quipped, "If I cuss you, you no go hear?"

It was a unique aspect of his father's personality—a shy, quiet man, he was nonetheless clever, responding to most criticisms with a quick wit and sharp tongue.

His knack for commanding an audience, even with his quiet voice, had brought his father to Miss Owen, an English missionary and vice principal of a secondary school in Oporoma, another small waterside community about twenty kilometers upstream from Ekowe along the circuitous River Nun. His father explained that Miss Owen had convinced a church in England to purchase the engine for his father so that his ministry could spread further with greater ease. His father had hosted a boat dedication and launching. Villagers gathered by the water's edge while his father held a Bible. Clad in a red and white robe, even Bishop Afonya had attended, holding his staff and placing his hand on the roof of the canoe to bless it.

The modified canoe had been a blessing to his work of spreading that good news, but perhaps there was another reason he'd received the motor when he had—perhaps this gift was meant to help Matthew achieve his destiny!

The trip to Warri would be dangerous on land. Soldiers roamed the countryside. A river route to Warri would allow them to travel only among the locals. It would be infinitely safer than traversing the land.

There was still some risk, of course. A war raged across the country. But, as his father reminded him, God had come through for him before. He had protected him from severe illness. He would protect him again.

It was very early in the morning and still quite dark when they loaded food and Matthew's suitcase into the canoe, along with a pair of paddles and a jerrycan of gasoline. As they carried their supplies down the path to the pier, the ground became softer, until he felt his feet sink into the mud at the edge of the river. The smell of the petrol fumes battled the aquatic scent of the river; the new technology of the motor juxtaposed with the sights, sounds, and smells of traditional Ijawland. With the boat loaded, they pushed off from the shore, launching into the River Nun.

His father's face filled with pride as he pulled the cord to start the motor. They plunged forward toward Warri, a winding, twisting path of rivers that curved across the land, stretching a 100-kilometer distance into three times that length, by Matthew's estimate. The water murky and brown beneath them, they steered northward, following a route his father had traveled many times. Standing sentinel, the tall palm trees wished them well, eventually, hesitantly, giving way to the mangrove forest, where sturdy trees perched atop their spidery roots and the fresh water turned brackish.

As a spray of river water wetted his face, the wave of nostalgia threatened to wash him away. He'd heard stories about himself as a very small boy. Sometimes, he'd been told, when the day was hot and his body strong, his mother would throw him into these waters. For a few seconds, he'd flail his chubby limbs, unattended and gasping for air, just as he'd seen many mothers toss their babies into the water, ensuring that they learned to swim just as surely as they learned to walk.

He'd been only a little older when she plopped him into her canoe. Out of necessity, his mother took him, snugly wrapped around her back in a traditional cloth as she ventured off to work the riverside farms.

She'd lacked the convenience of a motor, just as his father had until recently. So, as a child, he'd learned how to paddle by watching her. With sticks he'd gathered from the shoreline, he mimicked her motions, learning, through play, to propel the canoe through the water. By age eight, he could steer.

As he grew up, his need for river travel had been much less frequent, but he held close his memories of traveling the bustling river, people traveling in canoes and fishermen with their nets, even as he had slipped into the habit of road travel in the cities and towns.

As the waters delivered them into the River Forcados, which like the Nun split from the River Niger—the primary river in West Africa—he realized that this would always be his home.

The water was as familiar as the blood in his veins.

No matter how far he might wander in his lifetime, across Nigeria or around the world, his heart was tethered to this land of canoes, of close-knit community, and fierce wrestling competitions. Their route passed through one village after another, huts and docks jutted out into the water, people on canoes and children in the water. Tossing his net into the water, a fisherman nodded to the two. Matthew nodded back. Several meters ahead, two children splashed purposefully, masks of concentration on their faces. He recalled the refreshing sensation of plunging into the river as a child, the feeling of floating, the panic of being dunked, the gasped invitations to a water-wrestling match.

After seven hours on the water, his father increased the canoe's speed, pushing forward against the smoother waters that curved west along the state's border, and merged onto the northward path to Warri. Another hour remained until the two would climb from the boat and make their way to the path, then the road, that led to Hussey College.

His feeling of joy—of hope—was perhaps less new than it was refreshed.

Perhaps, he thought, they'd come through the worst of it.

Perhaps, things would soon return to normal.

Warri was a big city, considerably larger than Uzuakoli, and Matthew felt a renewed sense of optimism as they made their way through the city. They purchased some necessities, shared dinner together, and, most importantly, arrived at the school to make arrangements for his studies.

In the morning, his father returned to the waters of Ijawland and made his way back to the village.

There was a strange sense of familiarity in that—in once again being alone at school.

Matthew had been granted refuge in the Nigerian Civil War. While the war had not ended, here in Warri, he felt reasonably safe in the shelter of campus, his schoolwork a welcome distraction from the occasional anxiety of the world beyond the city's borders.

Once again, he was on the path to the life he'd imagined.

Chapter 4

SOLFÈGE

⁓

"EVEN THE WALLS HAVE EARS."

Judit couldn't remember the first time she'd heard the phrase. Even when she was too young to truly understand what it meant, it sounded ominous.

Now that she was a teenager, she understood, and it chilled her to the bone. The Communists were always listening.

Hungarians had enjoyed a very brief period of respite after the 1956 uprising. For the first time in years, they had been allowed to enroll their children in a variety of foreign language classes, the syntax of German and French and English like the opening bars of an enchanting sonata. There was hope.

But it was short-lived.

By 1957's first day of fall classes, Russian was again mandatory. And, while religion classes were still permitted after the uprising, to Judit's dismay, they were strongly discouraged. Church confessionals again became the only outlet where people could speak freely about religion and other forbidden topics, the cramped booths constructed from the only walls without ears—at least for the moment.

No one knew then how long their modicum of religious free-dom would hold out, so, of course, Judit sat eagerly in the front row of her Religious Studies class on her first day at Kaffka Margit Girls Secondary School.

It was a short walk from her home to the towering building on Villányi Street, but its grand, checkered floors and echoing vaulted ceilings transported her to a different world. When she filed down the hallways with the other girls, walking as they did in even, uni-form rows, the rhythmic patter of their shoes sounded like gentle spring rain. The very picture of order and obedience, the girls walked straight and tall in their tidy, dark blue dresses with their neatly concealed buttons and their crisp, white button-on collars.

Judit thought it was a fitting image. The school's namesake, Margit Kaffka, had also been modest in appearance but bold in action, authoring Hungary's most important—and perhaps most politically critical—literature.

But even though the building bore her name, as long as the country struggled under Russia's control, there would be none of Kaffka's defining political critique. No subject, however banal, could escape the sway of Communist propaganda, and history and geography explicitly glorified the Soviet Union. Even when they were supposed to be talking about Hungarian land or culture, teachers found a way to uplift the Soviets, ignoring the soldiers' many horrific atrocities.

Day after day, Judit and her fellow students learned of the Communist virtue as they sat obediently at their hard wooden desks, practicing Russian and reciting Marxist philosophy.

Given the prolific propaganda, one might think that all Hungarians were compliant.

One would be wrong.

Hungarians found all kinds of ways to resist—they just had to be careful.

One such time had come when she was in seventh grade, just thirteen years old, drifting off during the teacher's instruction as she often did. Eyes moony at the sunshine beyond the classroom window, she'd been reliving a recent summer trip to Vereb when a familiar name cut through her daze.

"Béla Bartók, you might be surprised to learn, was affiliated with the great Soviet campaign," the teacher announced.

Her teacher's eyes danced with the thrill of a juicy historical secret, but Judit's eyes had narrowed. Her maternal grandmother, Elza, was the famed composer's only sibling, and Judit considered his son, Béla, Jr., a second father. He and his wife—who shared a name with Judit, a fact that delighted the girl—lived just down the street in Budapest on Köbölkút Street.

It was Uncle Béla's love of nature that first truly fostered her humanistic personality, and the Bartók home that created in her a vision of an ideal future. The apartment echoed with clocks, all striking the hour precisely in unison, little birds popping out of little windows to signal the passage of time. Fresh flowers sang brightly, seemingly perched on every table in the apartment, and nothing ever seemed out of place.

She thought of their home as a hotel, but it was much more than that. It was a place she felt safe.

So when the teacher continued to inform the students about Bartók's supposed Communist sympathies, Judit grew deeply confused. The statement bordered on ridiculous. If Béla had traveled to the United States as an arm of the Soviets, as the teacher said, Judit didn't know of it. He seemed nice enough from what she had heard.

That day in class, the teacher had gone on to say scary things about Bartók—things at a harsh contrast to the Béla she knew—and his role in the "big Soviet Union." All the teachers used that phrase, an apparently harmless moniker, but one that had been deeply encoded with propaganda.

When she got home, she mentioned what happened, puzzled by the teacher's comments—she didn't understand why her parents seemed to dislike the Soviets if someone as close to them as Béla Bartók supported them! Something was amiss.

A few days later, she'd all but forgotten about the incident, consumed instead with a new song she'd heard, when her teacher retrieved a neatly folded letter from its envelope, smoothed the creases flat, and began to read.

The words that came from the teacher's mouth weren't her own—they were Uncle Béla's. "Béla Bartók," she read, "never played a role in any Soviet campaign. In fact, he would be horrified to learn of the statements made to a young, impressionable population of students."

The letter went on for some time, the teacher's face growing redder with each passing sentence, but Judit missed most of the letter's contents, cheering inside for a wrong so easily righted. Usually, in her short experience, justice came hard-fought—if it came at all.

Such was the case with the youth choir. As a pre-teen, Judit had gotten her first, sweet taste of the magic of singing, an experience that lasted until she was seventeen years old.

Growing up, she always had a fascination with music, taking private lessons to learn to play the piano, and later the descant recorder, but hadn't yet delved into the instrument of voice. She'd been twelve years old when she joined the youth choir at St. Imre's Church near the bottomless pond. The instructor Kornél Albert

Bárdos, a Cistercian priest as well as a music historian and teacher, had kind eyes, enhanced by his stylish round spectacles and his slightly balding head.

Bárdos—or Mr. Berci, as they called him—was a renaissance man who held an impressive array of degrees and a well-honed affinity for teaching children. Fired from his Cistercian priest service in 1951, he'd been sent to Miskolc. He had a doctorate degree in Hungarian, and possibly Latin, and worked as a solfège and music history teacher. Nevertheless, he continued to illegally run his youth choir in church with religious education.

Of course, Judit didn't know that then.

What she did know was that he made her want to sing her heart out.

Back then, she hadn't known solfège, the practice of assigning notes on the scale to various syllables—do, re, mi, fa, and so on—as a way to teach children aural and sight-reading skills. When Judit was a child, the practice wasn't yet taught in schools—but Mr. Berci had teased the technique with his students, helping them learn their parts by ear as a way of encouraging the pure, sweet vibration of a group singing in perfect unison.

Judit found herself completely enamored with the teacher's sight-singing lessons, following the notes of traditional folk music with rapt attention. Eager to please, she practiced her solfège scales relentlessly, sometimes prompting a grumpy sibling to snap at her when the do-re-do-mi-do-fa exercises got excessive.

She didn't care. Let them snap. She was determined to master this fascinating mix of music and mathematical precision, learning to control her voice beautifully.

Judit, along with the other children, gathered in the left side tower room of the church to rehearse every Monday. They regularly performed during mass, taking over for the adult choir who sang for the earlier mass. Despite the unlawful nature of hosting a youth choir, the parish priest looked the other way in solidarity with other religious leaders and allowed them to perform and continue lessons.

At the time, education was closely regulated, both in school and out. This was doubly true when it came to religious education—educators were not allowed to teach religion or even expose people to it. Priests weren't allowed to teach at all, as the government feared they would foster the development of religious thinking.

The government was right to be afraid. When Judit and the other teens, fifty or so in total including her close cousin Veronika, gathered around the priest, they did much more than sing. In his signature rapid-fire voice, Mr. Berci incorporated divinity lessons into choir practices, regularly interrupting practice sessions with religious monologues or sermons.

It was no small risk on his part. The government didn't revere priests. Often, they were actively discredited, with state agents spreading demeaning and perverse details about them. Sometimes the government gathered dirt on them by conducting house searches; other times, they just made it up. Priests who spent time with children were most frequently targeted, sent far away, where they couldn't influence the minds of the next generation of citizens. Convents, monasteries, and Catholic schools were seized. Within the clergy's ranks were so-called "peace priests," who were loyal to the communist regime and supported government policies. They were generally despised or ignored by the faithful.

Knowing all that Mr. Berci had risked to lead them in song and prayer, Judit was grateful, lapping up stories about David and Goliath, the Good Samaritan, and the Great Flood. That one scared her a little, in truth. But she loved the story of baby Moses, swaddled and placed into a basket of reeds, rocked to sleep by the lulling waters of the Nile until the Pharaoh's daughter could rescue him.

It reminded her of the stories she'd heard about her own childhood. Even though she could hear the fear in her mother's voice when she recounted those days in the early 1940s, she loved to hear about them. Unlike her mother's scarred memories, Judit's connection with those events came with the distance of second-hand telling, and to her, the stories sounded exciting.

"We didn't have anywhere to put you, *Cinke*," her mother told her as soon as she was old enough to understand. The pet name, which meant "titmouse," was given to her due to her small size. "I'd only had time to grab a few blankets, but there was nowhere for a baby to sleep. I begged your father to stay, but—" her mother shuddered a little at the memory, "—he ran upstairs. I was sure the bombs were about to fall."

Her mother's eyes always took on a glassy look when she described that time, the day after Christmas in 1944, when Budapest was surrounded by Soviet and Romanian armies, the road to Vienna seized. Hundreds of thousands of civilians as well as German and Hungarian soldiers were trapped in the city, and enemy planes flew overhead, low and ominous.

"The sirens kept blaring," her mother continued. "It was so loud. You screamed and screamed."

"What did you do?" Judit asked with wide eyes.

Her mother's face was a mask of pain and love—that was often the case when she recounted stories from the war. "There was nothing to be done," she said with a sad shrug. "Nothing any of us could do. We just went to the basement and hoped everything would be okay. All of us from the building were crammed into that space for seven months, praying. I'd been praying already. When your father went upstairs, I prayed for him, too."

"But then *Apu* came back!"

"He did." She nodded. "He brought your cot, and somehow you slept. You were so little. We were really worried about you."

"And the other babies?"

Her mother smiled warmly. "And the other babies," she said, her voice light again. "The grown-ups were whispering, but babies cried and fussed, how babies do. But once you were in your little wicker carriage, you were happy as could be." At that, her mother pinched her cheek playfully, and Judit affected a sour face, giggling in spite of herself and scrunching her shoulders into her pigtails.

Like most children, she loved hearing about herself as a baby. As she grew older, moving through primary school and into secondary lessons at Kaffka Margit, she grew to understand how terrifying the situation must have been for the family. She knew from hearing others talk about it that many feared she wouldn't make it. Her mother's milk had dried up by then and, at nine months old, she was emaciated and much smaller than she should have been. Her father had reassured them, he'd told her, saying that the baby was "as strong and resilient as her mother," a comparison that made Judit glow with pride.

She'd always been small—the baby of the family in every possible way.

As she learned in those illicit divinity lessons during youth choir, baby Moses had once been small, too. Yet he had grown up to be a great champion for justice, no matter how small and meek he'd once been. Not that she imagined herself becoming like

Moses—she could never be such a leader and didn't even aspire to be—but she wanted to be a good person and make others' lives better in the little ways she could.

She'd loved her time in youth choir. It had ended abruptly in 1961 when Soviet rules against teaching religion had begun to weigh heavy on religious educators like Mr. Berci. With constant threats from the government, it was difficult to be a religious figure, and he'd ceased his work as a priest.

During her time in the choir, she realized that investing in the combined interests of music and religious education represented a small act of righteous rebellion. It was a way of standing up for what was right against all odds.

It was then that she realized her true calling was the combination of music and teaching. She could do both just like Mr. Berci, and she would model her work after Kaffka Margit's beloved music teacher, D^2P^2.

Of course, D-squared P-squared wasn't his actual name. Years ago, a group of long-graduated schoolgirls had coined the silly name for Dr. Domokos Pál Péter, and Judit and her friends eagerly adopted it in turn. As skilled in ethnomusicology as he was in pedagogy, the man was the most engaging teacher at Kaffka Margit.

Dr. Domokos would call the class to order, as much order as there could be in the sea of excited pupils, and the students would listen hungrily as he explained the next exercise. Sometimes, they were simply told to sway from side to side as D^2P^2 sang to them, his voice as dreamy as his magnetic mannerisms. Others would practice singing a passage and, to their great delight, would be told they had mastered the exercise. Only then were they given instructions on how to notate the music they'd just sung.

Judit was hooked, frequently staying after class to visit with

D^2P^2. Sharing a mutual friend in Uncle Béla, the two formed a bond, as D^2P^2 encouraged her like no teacher ever had before.

It was the Kodály Method that really hooked her. It had only recently been introduced at a widespread level, D^2P^2 told her, and if she could master it, she could become one of its ambassadors, using the innovative techniques to teach children music with their precise developmental levels in mind.

The approach was elegant—too complex to be intuited, but, once one understood it, so simple one wondered why they hadn't thought of it before. With hand and body movements paired with each syllable of solfège, Kodály allowed children to capitalize on the way music made them feel. Their hands shifted upward as their pitch heightened and feathered down as their pitch lowered. It was bounded and clear while also being deeply expressive.

Through that sense of belonging, the bond of movement and sound with clear, defined, elegant rules, Judit discovered her calling. Like D^2P^2 and Mr. Berci and Uncle Béla, she would learn the art of music, weaving together the grand landscape of melody and notation to raise her voice to share her love with future generations. But more than that, she would help others to raise their voices, standing in the shadows of the brave nuns who had founded Kaffka Margit, only to be abducted by Communists twenty-eight years later. She would fight ferociously for the underdog.

She would not only love music. She would teach children to as well.

The little girl—that slim and sickly baby sleeping in the wicker bassinet while her parents feared for her life—had finally found her calling.

Chapter 5

AIM HIGH AND SHOOT HIGH

~

DILAPIDATED, THE STORIED RESIDENTIAL buildings that had looked so fresh and new now appeared to Matthew as blackened shells of their former selves. It had been three months since Port Harcourt had been liberated, and yet, soldiers still roamed the streets. Its electric grid destroyed, the city's hum fell quiet, exacerbated by sagging, abandoned homes and deserted neighborhoods. Many of the people of Port Harcourt had fled the city, seeking refuge in the villages of their ancestors, whatever modest possessions they could carry perched on their heads. The city wasn't exactly in ruins, but it looked very different from the last time he'd visited.

Still, Port Harcourt radiated hope. People had begun slowly filtering back to their homes. They scrubbed the soot from the walls and replaced shattered panes of glass, exclaiming with tearful joy at the return of neighbors and friends. Once a relentless monster, the miserable howl of war had been reduced to a specter—although it still loomed, soldiers in army fatigues with guns propped on their shoulders and camouflage trucks patrolled periodically. Almost as in defiance, the city had begun to straighten its spine and throw its shoulders back, in vain attempts to reduce the military presence to a simple nuisance.

It was difficult to trust it—so much hope set against so much blight—and Matthew feared he was just projecting his own optimism onto the city. Like Port Harcourt—like so much of Nigeria—he'd seen his carefully laid plans dashed to the ground, hollowed out by the rhythmic flurry of news headlines and bullet spray. In the face of disappointment, he'd gathered his strength and set one foot in front of the other. Whether or not he was imagining it, the city's confident footfalls, in lockstep with his own, bolstered him.

He'd learned to feel at home with "his people." From him, this was larger than just the Ijaw. In a way, he'd always felt this, proudly claiming three different villages. Under the historical Ijaw matrilineal culture, he was Ogbian. But his paternal grandmother claimed Nembe, and his grandfather Tombia. Matthew had always claimed all three.

And now, he lived in Port Harcourt.

He recognized its kindred spirit as the city reached out to him, her embrace feminine like the Ijaw God. In stark contrast to the strong-armed push and pull of war, Matthew felt a tenderness in the city. Amid its sharp corners and dense surfaces, the city was, at her heart, a nurturing presence. She'd guided him back here, and now she guided him to INEKIO.

A flyer posted near a school building, hand-written in bold red lettering, had informed him of INEKIO, a social organization for Rivers State student alumni. It read above an explanation that the word was an acronym, one letter for one or more of Rivers State's major tribes. As much out of curiosity as longing for community—although he certainly felt both—he'd pulled his neatly rolled newspaper from the back pocket of his tan trousers and scribbled the information on a spare corner. There would be an INEKIO social event in a few days.

A few days later, as he approached the large hall just outside Port Harcourt, he felt as much as heard the group's joy. Doo-doot, doot, bop-bah, scraped out the steel guitar, dominant over the tk-tk of fingers snapping and feet shuffling. A peel of laughter screeched through the music, answered by Cardinal Rex Lawson's horn, distorted by the metallic wah-wah of a Harmon mute. Drawn by the song's crooning call to set worry aside and focus on this moment, he floated into the backroom to find neat clusters of young men and women about his age.

Like a salve on his soul, this community radiated a spirit like his own.

Color and sound flooded the room. A thin woman in a red wrap skirt turned and smiled as he entered. To his right, a man laughed so hard he nearly spilled his drink. Another woman with a rounded figure and a halo of neatly-defined curls slipped in front of him—"excuse me," the woman said—then disappeared, replaced in his line of vision by a blue cotton mini-dress.

And then, Matthew spotted a familiar face. Making his way to the back corner, as his feet involuntarily tapped out the song's beat, he got a better look at the tall man in a long white tunic and baggy trousers. He looked like a fellow Methodist College student with whom he'd crossed paths on several occasions during his time in Uzuakoli, but Matthew was at a loss for his name.

As he approached, a dark-skinned man in a black top hat leaned against the wall, a green bottle with a big, white star cradled possessively in his hands. "Basically," the man was saying as Matthew came into earshot, "he's mocking Nigerian politics," he said, shaking his head.

Another man waved his hand dismissively. "Ah, come on, it's meant to be funny!"

The first man tilted his head in faux shock. "I don't find it funny at all."

"Only because you have no sense of humor!"

At that, the others erupted into laughter, the man in the top hat shooting them a playfully sour look.

Seizing the opportunity, Matthew stepped forward. "Give me one beer!" Closer now, he felt certain he recognized the man in white.

"Hey!" A wave of recognition washed across his face. "Did you go to Methodist College?"

The man grinned, a warm expression that set Matthew immediately at ease. "Yes! Abam."

"Ah, yes, I remember!" He took a beer from the man in the top hat, nodding in thanks. "I'm Matthew Mamah."

As the others introduced themselves, he cracked open the bottle and took a swig. Lawson's "Bere Bote," flowed seamlessly into a smoother beat.

"That is my song! He's an Ijaw man!" exclaimed Bassey, the man in the top hat. With short, choppy steps, he made his way into the center of the room, head swaying to the beat.

Abam stood at least six inches taller than Matthew, but his stature belied his humble warmth. "How have you been?"

The two hit it off immediately. Like Matthew, he'd set out to earn a university degree. Abam had been fortunate to finish his A-levels before violence spread to Uzuakoli, but, like Matthew, he now found few opportunities to continue his education. Here was where the men found their surest common ground—tenacious to their core, both refused to lower their standards in the face of the spiraling storm of revolution.

Matthew didn't remember much about Abam. Quite intelligent—Matthew felt surer of this the longer they talked—Abam had been in a few of his classes and hoped to achieve a graduate degree someday. He liked him immediately. Abam's ambitions mirrored his own. He reminded him why he'd always valued education—not only for the opportunities it provided, but because learning was, itself, an opportunity.

Perhaps it was his investment in educational access, as much as his need for income, that drove Matthew to his unusual post at the Holy Rosary Girls Secondary School, now rebuilding after the war had driven out the European nuns who ran it. In many cultural traditions across the country, girls weren't educated. From very young ages—five or six years old—many were socialized as domestics, as were his sister Comfort, his mother, and his grandmother before her. They spent their days cooking, cleaning, and tending to younger children, which freed the men up for school and the economic opportunities education provided. As a child, he'd benefited from his older sister's care, enjoying a life life with minimal domestic duties. It had all seemed normal back then, even proper. As a young man, he recognized the steep toll his sisters had paid for him—the sacrifice of their own hungry minds for his.

Education had lifted him out of the places he grew up. From Ogbia, where he lived until he was 10 years old, while his father was largely away for catechist and theological training, to Emelego, where the family moved after he was ordained a priest. But in each of these small towns, he'd seen how governmental disregard led to a lack of development, particularly compared with the amenities he enjoyed in Port Harcourt.

By the grace of his education, he enjoyed the luxuries of the city. By their sacrifice, his sisters had not.

So, when he heard that Holy Rosary was hiring a teacher, he not only saw a job—he saw a calling.

Long ago, Matthew knew, his father had been a teacher, too. As young as sixteen, his father taught at an Anglican school in Kolo, Ogbia. Later, once he was married, he'd moved with Matthew's mother to a neighboring Ogbian village called Otuokpoti where he'd turned his focus to pastoral duties.

His father held teachers in high regard, second only to clergymen. Before Matthew was born, he'd served as the former and, when Matthew was a child, he'd completed his theological training. Planting the seeds of Matthew's investment in education, he'd spoken fondly of his time as a headmaster and teacher. The community, his father often said, needed education. Otherwise, there could be no real advancement in society.

But his father was also much stricter than Matthew imagined himself to be. Along with his Bible, his father had carried a long cane carved from a tree branch, a clear signal to his students that he would discipline unruly children without hesitation.

When his father had sent him to Port Harcourt for grammar school, he'd warned Matthew about acting up. He recounted a tale of two young adolescents who dared to tussle in his father's presence. As headmaster, his father had been shocked to see the teens' clothing ripped and stained with reddish-brown earth as they rolled and grunted, scraping for the upper hand. The students had been shocked to see him, too, immediately jumping to their feet and mumbling the obligatory, "Sorry, sah!"

They could have left it at that, but as soon as his father had stepped away, the brawl resumed. With four swift whacks of the wooden cane, two for each of the boys, his father had made it clear that such behavior would not be tolerated in his school, whether or not his back was turned.

As a student Matthew had never been much of a fighter himself—he found it more effective to try disarming any potential foes with a clever line or his boisterous laugh. There had been no need to raise his fists as a boy. Neither did he see a need for physical punishment now that he was a teacher.

Most problems, he believed, could be solved with words.

Of course, it didn't hurt that he was a charismatic speaker. Never speechless, Matthew could conjure explanations from thin air, sometimes discovering the meaning of an event or idea as he spoke. The talent to command a room had always come easily to him, and as he'd progressed through grammar school and A-level studies, he'd grown even more confident in the power of a confidently-delivered message.

Like the plantain porridge his mother prepared as a treat, the sense of command—of a hundred eyes watching, a hundred ears listening—tasted sweet and rich and satisfying, pleasantly heavy in his gut. Perhaps he'd been predisposed to it—all those years of watching his father preach had whetted his appetite—but more likely, he believed, his passion for speaking aligned with his passion for education. When he informed others about the state of Ijaw politics, he felt swept away, the passion and purpose of those moments invigorating.

Matthew had always been complimented for his quick brain—a "computer mind," as Abam often called it. He often regaled his friends with animated analyses of Nigeria's two biggest issues:

tribalism and the colonial mentality. With the combined power of his wit, political savvy, and charm, sometimes a simple pronouncement could morph into a small, informal speech.

Such was the case at the next month's INEKIO event in Abonnema, requiring a boat ride across the state.

It started casually. The group had pooled their earnings to purchase a case of kai-kai, a cloudy, bisque-colored wine made from the sap of the area's abundant palm trees. Like fuel on the fire of their youthful camaraderie, the sweet liquid went down easily, perhaps too much so, and soon, Matthew was proselytizing about the plight of the Ijaws.

"They don't even talk about us!" he'd said, his voice rising in volume and force. "They ignore the Ijaw people in politics. But, of course, they're more than happy to siphon the oil from our land."

"Yes oh!" someone shouted.

He glanced over to find the voice's source and realized that a crowd had formed around him. The fire in his gut lit up. He pushed forward, more impassioned than ever.

"When will the Ijaws get our due? When will Rivers State finally earn the respect and support of our government? Rivers State produces all of Nigeria's crude oil, but our people are the poorest in the country. There is no electricity or clean running water in our villages."

Many in the group nodded, and someone let out an energetic, "Exactly!"

"Why can't we have what others have? Roads, electricity, accessible communication with the outside world?"

He paused for dramatic effect and the room went quiet. Just when the pause threatened to tip into discomfort, he quietly asked, "What is our greatest natural resource?"

"Oil," someone shouted, a murmur of agreement spreading amongst the crowd.

Only when the crowd was silent did he speak again, "Our greatest natural resource is education."

"Ahh," someone sighed.

"We are the richest region in the country. But until we ensure that every single Rivers State child receives an education, we should not be satisfied."

His firm words were enough to send the crowd into raucous applause. One man raised his cup, the contents sloshing onto his neighbor. At that, Matthew let out his signature laugh, leading the room back into the merriment of the evening.

As it turned out, Matthew would soon see firsthand that political will and education did not always go hand in hand. He arrived to work the next day, sharply dressed in a slim-cut jacket and tie, to find a scene that starkly contrasted the previous night's festivities.

Where he expected to see a classroom full of students, only rows of empty desks and a stale silence greeted him. The stone walls and wooden chairs only echoed the lack of talk and laughter. He straightened the papers on his desk, uncertain of what to do, before heading into the hallway. Everything appeared as it should, save for one student who was hurrying—nearly at a run—away from him and toward the building's exterior door.

"Hey!" he shouted. "Stop!"

"Sorry, sah!" Her pace slowed, but she did not stop.

"Come here," he replied with calm authority.

She turned and flashed him a pleading look.

"You're not in trouble. Just come here." He strode forward to meet her halfway, and begrudgingly, she followed suit. "Where are your classmates?"

She shrugged and looked longingly toward the door.

Face stern and eyes bright, an expression that always disarmed his students, he waited her out.

After a few moments, the truth spilled out of her. "They are angry, sah. They have to walk far to get water. They said they are not coming to class if they don't fix our water pipes for us, sah. I don't know, sah—"

He laughed, warm and generous, and the girl closed her mouth, wide-eyed and sheepish. "Let's go and see," he said. He forced a calm demeanor but inside, his nerves wailed.

Just as the girl had implied, the students from his class—and several others from the looks of it, had gathered in an ominous clump in the grass outside the school, uniformly dressed in blue blouses and navy skirts. He caught a smattering of angry words, a curse word, shouted despite their forbidden nature, rising above the din.

With a deep breath, he approached the girls. They grew silent as he got closer, nudging others around them to hush as well.

Finally, one bold student spoke up. "Sorry, sah, but they are not listening to us. We have reported and they have not done anything."

Impressed by the clarity and timbre of her response, he nodded, a calm gesture meant to camouflage his fear. For the first time, he wondered whether his father was right to carry a wooden cane, but, with none in sight, he would have to rely on his words.

"The problem is the lack of water?"

"Yes, sah!" she replied. In unison, the other girls echoed the sentiment.

"Will a riot solve the problem?" he asked.

"Yes—" the group's leader started, but a strong glance from Matthew interrupted her.

"Until they kick you out, and you have to go back to your village," Matthew remarked sarcastically. "Look, I will talk to the principal for you. Don't worry."

They chatted for several minutes, Matthew, ever charismatic, expressed his empathy and considered their point of view. He responded to their concerns and managed to convince them he was truly listening.

Slowly, the girls began to nod their heads.

"Now, back to your classrooms, all of you. You'll be late," he said, hoping he wasn't pressing his luck too far.

The crisis was averted, but Matthew was shaken. He liked teaching—or, at least, he saw the value in it—but he hadn't signed up for the role of disciplinarian.

And, perhaps more troubling, he hadn't planned to quash revolutions. Granted, the girl wasn't exactly Isaac Boro. Still, though he'd helped the girls in some way, he'd dismissed them from advocating for themselves. He believed in advocacy, despite his avoidance of political agitation, but he also knew that they needed a solid education before they could make a difference.

Perhaps, he thought, the universe had sent the girls as a signal, a message for him that it was time to resume his own trajectory.

And then, another sign from the universe, a post caught his eye. The bulletin board at the four-story Secretariat on Station Road was used as a center for employment and educational opportunities displayed in colorful flyers. He and Abam went to review the postings, and stapled there was an announcement—all Rivers State youths were invited to apply for new foreign scholarships.

As it turned out, his speech to INEKIO—not unlike his confrontation with the girls in the schoolyard—had been timelier than he knew. The Rivers State government had set its eye on educational improvements. Under the leadership of a military governor not much older than Matthew, the city had determined that investments in education were investments in the state's development. While the war pulsed on in Nigeria, other countries enjoyed stable, predictable university educations.

Matthew enthusiastically completed the application, his mind dancing with visions of a shining new city, columns of ivory and marble rising up before him.

Abam's vision was somewhat more dismal. "You'll get an interview, I'm sure. I doubt I will."

"Mpschww!" he dismissed his friend jokingly. "We will get it. Both of us."

"Maybe," Abam laughed. "Maybe to Siberia or Iceland."

But Abam was wrong, at least about the interviews. Both men, along with over fifty other applicants, were invited to speak with the state scholarship board.

Sweating under his dark blue tie, Matthew tried to breathe deeply, but his heart leapt into his throat when a man in a dark suit opened the door. Through the open door, Matthew could see Ken Saro-Wiwa, the new education commissioner, sitting in the back of the room to observe interviews. Dressed in traditional Nigerian attire, he looked even younger than Matthew had expected. Educated at the prestigious University of Ibadan, with teaching experiences in Ibadan and Nsukka, Saro-Wiwa had a keen interest in education and the cultural arts. His stint teaching in African literature at the University of Nigeria, Nsukka, had been interrupted by the war, and he returned to Port Harcourt for public service.

Saro-Wiwa looked up, his eyes connecting briefly with Matthew's, just as the other man flipped over a sheet on his clipboard and called, "Matthew Mamah."

He'd been holding his breath, he realized. With palms clammy and heart racing, Matthew nodded to Abam—his friend's smile warm and reassuring—took a deep breath, and made his way into the interview room.

Chapter 6

DEATH OF A DREAM

⁓

D
RAPED ACROSS HER BED, JUDIT wondered
whether anyone had ever felt so alone. She knew she
had a family who loved her—she'd never doubted that.
And yet, heart heavy and stomach sour, she couldn't conjure the
energy to pick herself up and go about her life as though everything was fine.

Her two north stars, music and her faith, felt like the only true
constants in her life—in the entire world. Now they were disinte-
grating before her eyes, draining through her fingers like fine sand
as she struggled to contain even a single grain of her truth.

It was like being pulled in opposite directions.

Throughout her time at Kaffka Margit, Judit had cherished her
religious studies classes. She loved learning Biblical stories and
studying Catholic theology, diving deep into the meaning of the
universe. Besides her time with D^2P^2, those classes were her favorites.

In the end, it turned out, they were her undoing.

She'd asked the school's administration for a formal recommendation, a baseline requirement for applying to all Hungarian

teacher education programs. When she'd been called to the school's main office, she assumed it was to pick up the letter.

Instead, lips thin and stern, the principal had delivered a devastating blow: her enthusiastic participation in religion courses precluded her from teaching. She wouldn't even be allowed to apply.

The news took her by surprise. Of course, she'd known that religious studies courses were frowned upon by the government. Administrators had vaguely warned the students that there were risks associated with that particular course of study.

But nothing so serious as this—no formal announcement that religious studies courses would limit students' future career prospects. Blindsided, she could hardly believe it.

Yet, there she sat as the principal delivered the news. There would be no formal recommendation. With no formal recommendation, there would be no education courses, no degree, and no teaching job.

She'd protested, of course, the heat of injustice burning like wildfire through her limbs. Nothing could be done.

Her dream had ended.

Face wet with tears, Judit asked her mother for advice, hoping in the vain hope of a child that she could make everything right. Instead, her mother's mouth had pulled into a thin line, much like the principal at Kaffka Secondary, as she silently pulled Judit into a hug.

She was angry and hurt by what had been taken from her. Her mother's face wore the same pain and disappointment that had been settling in Judit's gut since she'd gotten the terrible news. There was nothing they could do.

She'd taken to sight singing like a fish to water, and it felt good to finally find her purpose. She knew she would never be as beautiful and elegant as her eldest sister, Aci, or get married and start a family as young as Bori. Dull-haired and prone to distraction, Judit had long given up on replicating her sisters' perfect lives.

But she was the best sight-singer in her music school class, her voice moving effortlessly with the dots on the staff. She was half-way decent in piano and painting, but this was the first time she'd really excelled at anything.

Now, it was over.

As the rest of her graduating class excitedly planned their futures, she lolled through her days, listless and despondent.

Some mornings, her fingers seemed to gravitate to her rosary, moving as smoothly over the line of beads as they did through the notes on the scale. Ten Hail Marys followed by the Our Father followed by ten more Hail Marys, she prayed, seeking answers as much as she sought the inherent comfort of those familiar, predictable words.

If not for her love of those prayers she'd early studied in religion courses, she might have been able to follow her dreams.

In a way, it was ironic. She'd spent years immersing herself in religion—a lifetime, really—so when the government tried to take it away, instead it only drove her deeper into her faith. The faithful path gave her hope even as it crushed her planned future.

She simply could not reconcile a world that would offer her the gift of music with one that would deny her the opportunity to share it with others. Still, she listened. And as spring turned to summer and summer turned to fall, she could only see a future of doldrums.

She took a job as a laboratory assistant at a paint and varnish factory in Budapest, more as a way to stay busy than anything else. She hoped, of course, that she would somehow find herself in this new work, but the attempts to uncover some hidden identity always felt weak-willed, no matter how hard she tried to push herself.

And yet, to her surprise, she found that the job interested her. Her heart still ached for the future she'd imagined as a music teacher, but there was something compelling about how chemicals mixed and mingled and formed completely different substances.

Naturally inquisitive, she loved the challenge of figuring out how things worked.

Perhaps that was what drew her to solfège in the first place, with its clear rules and patterns. It made plain the miracle of written music—how lines and dots and symbols produced soaring concertos and charming folk songs that encapsulated entire cultures.

The more she thought about things that way—considering her inquisitive nature and curiosity about the inner workings of ordinary things—the more it made sense to her. From the time she was a young child, she'd been curious. She'd watched with fascination as her mother butchered chickens for the family's dinner. The meal was always a rare treat, given the expense of meat, let alone a whole bird. Judit particularly liked the opportunity to examine the chicken. Headless and reduced to pebbled skin, the chicken was no longer alive, but still had the mechanics of its living counterpart—the once-beating heart and once-breathing lungs, now deflated, all of these complex organs once functioned to keep such a small thing alive.

Maybe, she thought, there was something to be said for taking that curiosity beyond the realm of music. Although she still dreamed of teaching children—truly, she could never imagine herself feeling confident enough to teach, or even supervise, adults—she could see a lot of value in science. It wasn't so different

from music, in a way. Particular recipes produced particular results. The key was finding precise combinations and replicating
them—a deceptively difficult task that made it all the more rewarding.

If she could not teach, then perhaps she could try science.

With a nagging feeling in her gut, a mourning pain that never
seemed to dissipate, she found the motivation to take the entrance
examination for the Budapest Technical University.

She tried to conjure the expected level of enthusiasm—I could
be a chemical engineer! How exciting!—and hoped that she could
force herself to feel authentically eager by the start of the program.

But just when she watered the seed of enthusiasm, the universe
countered with a cruel joke—a letter that read, "Thank you for
your application to the Budapest Technical University. We regret
to inform you…"

She stopped reading and, with a burst of rage that surprised
her, wadded the letter into a ball and hurled it across the room.
With everything stacked against her, she felt furious and sad, disappointed and hopeless. She was determined to bury her pain as
best she could.

Over the next few days, she went about life as though it were
normal to feel the heavy weight of failure on one's shoulders, day
and night, hour after hour. She tidied her short brown hair and
straightened her modest dress in an attempt to feign contentment.
She carried her grief with her to visit friends, as she stopped at the
shops, and when she dropped in to see Uncle Béla and Aunt Judit.

Uncle Béla answered the door, his grin wide as he ushered her
back to the sitting room. The home reminded her of her childhood, a fantasy land walled with encyclopedias and sprinkled with
assorted chocolate candies that were rare in other homes. On that

day, the glimmer and promise of the Bartóks' ways seemed duller, dampened by her cloudy mood.

She forced herself to make small talk, to update the couple on her life—or, more accurate, the lives of her family. Determined not to burden anyone else with the disappointment of her failure, she held in the bit of news that embarrassed her most: she'd lost not one, but two plans for her life, and, increasingly, she felt certain that there was nothing else. She was doomed to live a life without purpose.

When the conversation lulled, Uncle Béla looked at her, eyes piercing. "Jutka," he said in that smooth way of his. He paused for some time, studying her face until she looked away, certain he could see right through her façade. "You're not yourself today."

She glanced up and feigned a smile. He didn't return the expression, his concern carving thin lines in his forehead.

Béla and his wife, Judit, knew, of course, of Kaffka Margit's refusal to write the recommendation—Béla had audibly gasped when Judit told them that the principal had said she would "spoil children against atheism," replying, "I should hope so!"

She refused to pour more of her sorrow on them, but that raised the question, then, of how to respond to Uncle Béla's query—she wasn't herself, that was true, and she wasn't sure she would ever be herself again.

"Everything is fine," she replied, forcing her expression to lighten.

She'd gone to the Bartóks' to visit, just as she always did, and now they were finished. Gathering her things, she wished them both a good evening and trudged back to her family's home.

Only a few days later, she finally received some good news. The university had reconsidered her application and accepted her to the chemical engineering department. Almost inexplicable, their change of heart shocked Judit to her core. Later she would learn that composer Béla Bartók's widow, Ditta Pásztory, had called the university and asked them to review her application.

At that moment, though, all she cared about was building a new dream. It wasn't what she'd hoped for, but it would have to do. One year after her graduation from secondary school, she attended her first class in the grand, stone building at the corner by Gellért Square.

Suddenly, it seemed that things might turn around.

One day after classes, Judit found herself boarding the bus at the same time as a girl wearing leg braces with a cane at her side. The girl expertly maneuvered up the stairs with no help from the disinterested bus driver, and, without thinking, Judit put down her bag and bumped the girl's walking stick.

Urgently apologizing, Judit reached up to steady the girl's elbow and ensure her thoughtlessness did not make her lose her balance. The girl, whose name turned out to be Ági, beamed at Judit and laughed. She was jostled all day long; such a little bump would not topple her.

The two shared an instant connection—Ági was about the same age as Judit, with longer brown hair and a pretty smile, and also a student at the university. While she was quite a good student, many of the aging transportation options in Budapest presented challenges for her. Passionate about serving others, Judit cherished the opportunity to help.

Perhaps, she thought, this was her purpose—to help the downtrodden. Most of their classmates didn't give Ági a second look, avoiding her socially so they wouldn't have to assist with the more inconvenient aspects of spending time with a disabled person.

That never bothered Judit at all. She'd always found joy in uplifting society's underdogs. It was who she was.

The idea buoyed her for a while. It was, at least, something to focus on. More and more, she found that she couldn't stand to think about the future. The only way she could actually enjoy the program was to ignore the fact that it was meant to prepare her for an engineering career.

She couldn't imagine herself becoming an engineer. That harsh reality clung to her, draining her motivation like a leech.

The weight of it accompanied her on her first trip out of the country, traveling to Kraków, Poland. She'd never left Hungary before, and the exhilaration was electric. With some relief, she felt the grip of dread loosening.

Her group had gone hiking one day, trudging through the forest and admiring the gorgeous scenery. When they reached a clearing, an opening in the trees that looked out over the vast expanse of mountains and the river below, Judit's eyes filled with tears. The weather was perfect, a hint of cool in the air to keep the sun's warmth at bay, but still, bright white patches of snow dotted the craggy hills as they swooped down to meet the water's glassy surface.

She could have stood gazing at the sight all day.

But the others quickly grew anxious. They seemed to her to be more typical young adults than she. They had big plans—there was always something to do, someone to see, some grand future to prepare for.

So she trudged on that day. And, every day, she trudged forward into her future.

Back to school she went, pushing away her disappointment, even as her schooling stalled. A few years into her program, she took an official break, accepting a job as a lab assistant.

That break turned out to be one more major issue in an academic career that felt like an insurmountable pile of problems. She hadn't been a particularly prosperous student, given the tug she felt to find a more fulfilling path. If she wanted to remain in school, her advisor warned, she'd have to make up the time. He recommended night classes. For the next several weeks, she spent days and nights at school, the pressure of finishing the degree grating against her waning interest.

The harder she pushed herself, the less passionate she became. Surely, she hoped, this could not be what life was all about.

Sometimes she wondered if she was going crazy. Her Nanya—the moniker she and her sisters used for their grandmother, Elza—was known for her anxious personality. Nanya worried about stores running out of food, so she bought things early. She worried about her health, so she constantly bothered her doctor. When someone wasn't home when she thought they'd be, she imagined them stuck under a tram.

Maybe, Judit thought, she suffered from the same malady.

Her family would never call Judit a disappointment—nothing even close to that—but she worried that they thought it. With clear purpose and direction, her sisters had set about their paths, building impossibly happy families and careers. Even her parents, who'd persevered through all sorts of political turmoil, had managed to effortlessly discover their purpose on this earth. Her father had even fought in World War I, receiving the national Order of Vitéz for his valor and chivalry as a soldier.

She would have laughed at the contrast if it didn't make her want to weep—never, in a million years, would chemical engineering give her that kind of drive and purpose.

Most days, she wasn't sure she was even capable of doing the work.

She tried to tamp that thought down, cramming it into the farthest corners in the back of her mind, but still it loomed there, bitter and threatening.

The longer she tried, straining under the pressure to juggle work and school, the heavier the weight of failure became.

"Don't you want to get on with your life?" her mother asked, the gentleness of the question only sharpening its sting. "Perhaps find a more stable career?"

Her father's questions felt gruffer, although she knew they came from the same place of care. "When's graduation?" he prodded. "Are you keeping up with your work?"

But it was Bori, her face taut with concern, whose questions burned hottest. "Have you met any boys?"

The most innocent of queries, it sent a jolt through Judit's core that wasn't easily shaken. Her twenty-fifth birthday had come and gone, and while, yes, she had met some boys, none of them showed real potential for marriage.

So she prayed over it. If only she could find a decent husband, it might buy her a bit more time to get her career in order. It was too much to ask, she knew, that God would drop the perfect man from the sky.

But she hoped He would.

Chapter 7

BUDAPEST

⁓

THE WORLD LOOKED DIFFERENT FROM high in the air. From the plane, the rivers snaked and squiggled, deep, mossy green against Lagos' textured taupe. The swirl of tan and green soon faded into the bleached orange of sandy mountains, which morphed into the richest blue Matthew had ever seen.

Suddenly, the plane shuddered. Engines still roaring, it descended as Matthew's heart leaped into his throat. Had it really been ten hours? He'd been lost in thought, alternating between a new issue of Newsweek and the stunning view, and somehow, they'd come to the end of their journey.

Streaked like marble with rivers, the green he saw below mirrored the Nigerian countryside. Except, he realized as they grew closer to the earth, these weren't rivers. Neat squares of brown, green, and amber jutted together in an intricate pattern, but the lines between them were roads. As they descended lower and lower toward the earth, the roads converged into a dense network, studded with tiny houses that grew larger and larger until the plane seemed to slap against the ground, bouncing for a moment, then slowing quickly, the force pressing him against his seat.

Not so different from the Lagos airport, the Budapest airport glowed, fluorescent lights illuminating clean, gray lines and tiled floors. It was the people that marked the difference here. His plane had carried passengers of various races and ethnicities from the diverse city of Lagos, but he'd begun to stick out more against the European crowd of his connecting flight. With pale skin and wide cheekbones, the people of Budapest overflowed with homogeneity.

It wasn't just appearance, either.

The airport echoed with a particular cadence as fascinating as it was unfamiliar. Infrequently interrupted, long strings of rounded vowels were occasionally cut short with a crisp ts sound. It rang in his ears like the sea, the roar of the crowd all ahs and shhs, unfamiliar and strange. For as long as he could remember, he'd spoken several languages and dialects. But he couldn't make sense of what he heard, the patter like no language he'd heard before.

From the airport, he boarded a bus. The sights of Hungary whizzed by, all curves and arches and tall, towering buildings, and he craned his neck to peer out the windows, his forehead smudging on the glass.

Back home, he'd seen himself as a sophisticated intellectual. He had now traveled farther than anyone he knew from back home. With an involuntary raise of his eyebrows, a hiccupping laugh escaped his lips. Port Harcourt had seemed impossibly chic only a few short years earlier.

How quickly things changed. Back then, his feet felt best barefoot. Now, the suitcase on the bus floor next to him contained several pairs of hard-soled shoes along with a growing collection of ties. Patterned with stylish colors and prints, overcoats, vests, and crisp bell bottoms were all neatly folded into his suitcase.

His clothing was stylish, but he rarely stood out in a Port Harcourt crowd.

Then he'd gone back home. Eager to share the good news of his scholarship with his father, he'd traveled to the village. His parents had separated, his father moving to take a position as Superintendent Priest at St. Mark's Church. And in Ekowe, even Matthew's most casual clothing seemed out of place.

"Papa, I got the scholarship," he'd announced, suddenly very aware of the nearly empty house his father inhabited alone. It was quiet, so unlike the bustling home of his childhood. "I'm moving to Hungary."

His father's face had lit up, an unfamiliar expression of surprise and delight. As he waited for him to respond—to congratulate him or say anything at all—Matthew realized his father had tears in his eyes. "My son," he finally said, squeezing his hands.

"There's a one-year language program, to learn Hungarian," he'd continued, "then to university."

Rising from his chair, his father looked older than Matthew remembered, but he'd strode into the next room, springing on the balls of his feet like an eager child. He'd returned with a wad of worn pounds.

While the scholarship paid for most of the program, Matthew was expected to contribute enough to cover some expenses. Fiercely independent, he preferred to take care of things on his own. But he needed the money, so he'd taken it without protest. There was no point in questioning it anyway—his father had known a contribution would be needed, handing over as much as he could for his son's education.

Where he'd grown up, most people didn't attend university. He was more fortunate than most, he realized, to have even attended grammar school. Certainly, he'd received opportunities that his sister hadn't. Again, he wondered what she would have done if not for the responsibility to care for him and their younger sisters, Dorcas and Ruth. Smart and conscientious, she would have certainly excelled in grammar school if she hadn't been so busy at home.

This was the experience of most girls in his village. By the time they could attend any kind of advanced schooling, they'd set their minds to domesticity, a habit as stubborn as it was socially desirable.

Comfort had pushed against this more than most, building herself a good life as an elementary teacher in the town of Bori. Her calm and peaceful presence made her a perfect fit for the task.

She'd been his next stop as he toured the countryside by canoe, stopping to announce his good fortune to his friends and family. Springing to her feet with a high-pitched squeal that reminded him of their mother, Comfort had danced over to hug him, so excited he couldn't help but laugh.

She, too, had handed him several more pound bills.

"*Bei taye o?*" he asked, although, of course, he already knew. What is this?

"You'll need money there. Things are expensive in the city." He'd chuckled a bit, and she gave a small smile, glancing at the ground. "What?" she asked, indignant. "I know about the city."

"Oh?" he grinned.

She raised her eyebrows before changing the subject. "Anyway," she said. "This is for you. I knew that you will get the scholarship."

He'd beamed at her, thanking her without words as she rambled on with her explanation.

"Papa said you will need some money when you went, so I want to give what I can to help. Okpoma," she said, suddenly serious.

He furrowed his brow then. Instead of the celebratory tone he'd expected, his sister's voice turned deathly serious. "What?" he asked.

"You're the big hope for our people."

He hadn't fully realized what that meant at the time, but as he stepped off the bus and into the bustling center of Budapest, her words burned behind his eyes. Always confident and cool under pressure, he was surprised to feel a hint of butterflies in his stomach, a faint tingle that radiated excitement peppered with nerves.

The feeling was familiar. He remembered visiting Port Harcourt for the first time and marveling at the newness of it all.

Anything but new, Budapest had a different energy. The buildings lurched high into the sky, but they weren't modern inventions. Instead, built by hands long since passed, the arches and finials whispered their history.

He'd been proud of the progress of Port Harcourt.

Now, he found, he was awed by the historic beauty of Europe. And yet, Budapest wasn't entirely old, either. Trams, as the Hungarians called them, whizzed by on intersecting rails that dug deep into the cobblestone streets. The trams were very different from the buses of Nigeria. Boxy and yellow, elongated with hinges to allow turns, they operated by electricity from cables above. No stray arms or shoulders hung from the vehicles' sides—the windows were paned. People sat quietly aboard the fantastical machines, reading newspapers or chatting casually as though they didn't comprehend the miraculous invention that shuttled them from one point to another.

And then he saw the water.

Matthew knew water. He'd grown up around water. Just a short walk from his dormitory, he'd thought the Danube would ground him in its familiarity. But while the clean, squared-off lines of the housing complex reminded him of a few of Port Harcourt's business buildings, the river was unlike anything he'd seen before. As clear as a mirror, the city's majestic buildings seemed to gaze at themselves in its reflection.

While the river felt unfamiliar in its grandeur, it also felt reassuring. He felt safe here.

He'd persisted through coups and revolutions and civil war, and, while he'd never felt particularly frightened, tension hung steadily in the Nigerian air. Here, people moved without a care in the world. They strolled down the street, arms loaded with paper and reusable cloth bags, and others sat, perched on bicycles that whizzed down alleys and wove through clusters of sightseers. He spotted the occasional couple displaying affection. He was surprised to realize how much he had come to accept the political tension in Nigeria—it had become a part of his everyday life.

Budapest seemed simpler—old and new and calm and beautiful, as though war could never touch this idyllic land with its idyllic people and their idyllic opportunities.

His idyllic opportunities.

On the first day of class, Matthew joined the trickle of students filtering into the classroom. The group quickly divided into smaller clusters, sorting itself by nationality—a Ghanaian group in the corner, several Polish groups at the far side of the room, and Nigerians clustered in the center. Bulgarians, far closer to home than Matthew, chatted easily with one another, while Lithuanians and Russians found seats in the back of the class.

And there they sat, seven hours per day, practicing Hungarian. It took him weeks to master the basics of the language.

"*Máté*," the middle-aged teacher called, turning his name Hungarian as was customary in his new country. "*Hogy vagy?*"

"*Jól vagyok*," he answered quickly. It was an honest answer—he truly was doing well, not only in acclimating to his new country but also in mastering the language. Having grown up switching between languages and cultures, he had a knack for new dialects.

"*És te hogy vagy tanárnő?*" Matthew quickly responded, returning the question.

Then, he paused. While most of his new language came relatively easily for him, *magázás* was a difficult, if fascinating, concept. A puzzling formal version of the language, magázás compounded the challenge of Hungarian's unique syntax by adding hidden rules of formality. Formal Hungarian required speakers to use third-person pronouns when speaking with someone in a position of power. This aspect, in particular, was driven home for the students, lest they accidentally address one of their professors with disrespect.

"*Hogy van a tanárnő?*" he corrected his question with a confidence that belied his struggle.

"*Kitűnő!*" she exclaimed, beaming.

Within just a few months, Matthew would have been comfortable speaking with other students in Hungarian. His fellow students, on the other hand, struggled, typically defaulting to English for their everyday conversations, a preference that allowed him to weave in and out of various groups, building new connections along the way.

One of these connections was a new student from Uganda. Venance was short, about Matthew's height, with thick, dark-rimmed glasses and dreams of agricultural engineering that mirrored his own. Together, they explored the city, wondering at Hungarian oddities, many of which Matthew would have overlooked if not for the brash social mannerisms of so many Hungarians. Here, first and last names were reversed, a fact that mattered little to Matthew who had gone by his last name for most of his adult life. But he soon found that people here reacted curiously to his last name.

"What kind of a name is Mamah?" Hungarians would ask, snickering amongst themselves. "Mamah?"

Never at a loss for words, he would reply with a sly grin, "It's the only word that means the same thing in every language. The same in all the villages in Africa as in the biggest cities in Europe!"

The comment never failed to disarm any trace of mockery in their voices, usually resulting in stunned silence.

Some Hungarians revealed through their questioning a bizarre fascination with his cultural background. "How many wives do you have?" they would ask. "How many sisters?"

Hungarians, he realized, traditionally asked about one's family, but it was more than that. Driven by his very dark complexion, their curiosity about Africa seemed to disarm the politeness typical of Hungarian culture. Referring to blacks as "*néger*," a word that was neither meant nor taken as an insult, they would pepper him with questions. He soon realized that they had no idea what it meant to live in Nigeria. They had no concept of the range of cultures or the differences between cities and villages in Africa.

So, he concocted a sarcastic response. "In Africa," he would say, his face still as stone. "I lived in trees with monkeys." They would stare, blinkingly slowly as he continued, "We swing from tree to tree there."

In these situations, he usually broke the silence with laughter, disarming those with harmful intentions and endearing himself to his friends.

It helped that Matthew spoke English with unusual clarity. Venance had once asked him why he spoke so differently from other Nigerians, impressed with his refinement and grammar. Venance was even more impressed with his command of Hungarian. While others in the class struggled, Matthew soared.

"I honestly don't know how you do it," his friend commented one day over lunch.

Matthew dipped the hard bread into his fisherman's soup. A new favorite dish of his, the *halászlé* tasted of the rivers, and while he'd never had paprika before, the flavors of fresh Hungarian fish made him think of home.

He'd almost acclimated to Hungarian food, although it had surprised him at first. Unlike the stew-like soups he would eat in Nigeria with eba or yam fufu, he'd found that Hungarians ate brothy soups with crusty bread, the texture a stark contrast with the soft, sweet breads of his home.

"How do I do what?" Matthew replied.

"Fit in so well," his friend said. "Your language is nearly perfect—you don't flinch at all with these strange culture things…"

He shrugged. "It's not that strange."

Matthew enjoyed learning about Hungarian culture. He liked hearing Hungarians talk, listening to the nuances of the language, now that he could discern meaning. Though Venance had complimented his grasp of language, accents sometimes still made things difficult. Some words with an African accent even breached into the profane: pronouncing "bus" in English or "sör"—the Hungarian word for beer—produced sounds that mimicked Hungarian curse words.

Not that he would ever let on, but he knew what Venance meant. Part of his "aim high, shoot high" motto meant fearlessly confronting unfamiliar situations. By its very nature, aiming high meant encountering new things, and he'd learned to navigate change with ease.

Someday, he knew, he'd use the skills he gained here to repay Comfort and his father. He'd finish out the year and move on to university, then return to Port Harcourt. At least, that's what he thought he'd do. The longer he lived abroad, the less certain he was about his future, seeing larger and larger opportunities in the expansive landscape of Hungary.

For now, he contented himself with enjoying the city. The smoothness of butter, the spices of salami, the warm, filling flavors of paprikash, and the opportunities granted him here that he'd never quite been able to capture back home.

And then, like a sudden start in the night, the intensive course was over. His cohorts had traveled together relatively often, attending recreational activities as well as those for promoting Communism. They played soccer and laid on the beach for hours—although Matthew and the other black students had quickly learned that this resulted in night sweats and vowed never to try it again.

As the program drew to a close, they were rewarded with one special trip. The crowd of their classmates disembarked from the train and onto the grounds of Kiliántelep, knowing that the two-week vacation would be the last time some of them saw one another.

He made his way to a short brick wall overlooking Lake Balaton and sat. He watched the swarms of students and other vacationers as recreational boats zig-zagged across the crystal blue lake.

"Man, the son of my father!" Venance said, plopping down next to him. "I wasn't sure where you went!"

He smiled at his friend, suddenly a bit nostalgic. Venance wouldn't travel far to university, assigned to attend the Hungarian University of Agriculture and Life Sciences in Gödöllő, just northeast of Budapest, but Matthew would depart the resort for a smaller town southwest of the capital.

"So! You're headed to Veszprém!" Venance continued, a lilt in his voice. "Are you ready?"

"Of course!" he replied, not really considering the question. "I've been ready. For a long time." He stood and stretched his arms toward the clear, blue sky, speckled with billowing clouds. This life, he thought, he could get used to.

Chapter 8

CHEMISTRY

~

A THIN, ROUND BRICK CHIMNEY PEERED down at Budapest's Harangozó Street, bold and proud. On a clear day, its bright red stripes shouted for attention, offset by a white background and the pale blue skyline. The structure was quite beautiful, although, unknown to Budapestians at the time, it poured a steady stream of highly toxic pollution into their air.

They wouldn't learn that until much, much later, though. In the early 1970s, nobody thought much about air pollution.

Water pollution, on the other hand, was stringently regulated.

Judit knew that well—it was her job to know. She reported to the factory every day to supervise Metallochemia's environmental impact. Over the past several years, she'd built her reputation in the company as a conscientious worker who cared about both her fellow employees and the environment.

She hadn't yet finished her degree when the company hired her in 1967. Back then, she worked dutifully as an Energy Department Officer, even as she struggled to believe she was qualified for the job. She'd hoped then that earning her degree would give her a boost of confidence. Four years later, after balancing a grueling schedule of night classes and full-time work, she finally graduated. While she felt proud of her accomplishment, she found that not much changed. She'd been studying at the university for eight years by then, and, although her diploma proved her skill in chemical engineering, she still wasn't sure it was her true life's purpose.

And then, surprising herself as much as anyone, she'd enrolled in—and completed—a post-graduate program.

She quickly rose through the company's ranks once she had a Master of Science degree in hand, and, in 1971, Metallochemia promoted her to the Central Laboratory. As close to passion as she'd experienced since graduating high school, the job became much more interesting. She did some product analysis and raw materials work, both interesting in their own way. Even better, she was tasked with running regular pollutant tests on the water that flowed from the Central Steam Plant's boiler, which gave her enormous pride for the undeniably noble cause of environmentalism at the heart of her position.

The plant's layout was complicated, less like a single, cohesive company than a cooperative of small, individual factories—each of them a potential culprit in any positive pollutant test. Yet, somehow both simple and complex, the testing process was elegant, the same trait that had drawn her to the field in the first place.

Small things like that drew her to the work. An inferior substitute for passion, certainly, but a sense of making a difference—of helping people—made the work sustainable.

That was all she'd ever wanted to do—help people. Even when she'd imagined herself a music teacher, it grew as much from her desire to help people as her love of music. She'd always loved music, of course. The greatest equalizer, music carried hope and comfort and promise for the future. But when she'd imagined herself in front of a classroom of children, as she often had growing up, she'd always seen it as a way to impact the world.

Her Metallochemia work wasn't about music, but it was about changing the world. For now, that would have to be enough.

So she diligently ran each sample, and, if any returned with pollutants, she wrote to the offending department with a warning.

A natural humanitarian, she excelled at that part of the job. She genuinely cared about others—not only the local communities who would be impacted by chemical spillage, but also the other workers in the buildings across the plant. She knew everyone was doing their best, so there was no reason to come down too hard on anyone.

She sent friendly memos detailing the pollutant levels alongside the regulatory guidelines. Most departments reciprocated her generosity and corrected problems swiftly and completely, avoiding any government sanctions.

While she loved the idea of preserving the environment—it was, after all, a way to support the less fortunate—chemical engineering would never be her passion. She'd have to find fulfillment beyond her career. With little sense of where to find it, she spent her time enjoying music and socializing with friends, and meeting new and fascinating people through her work at Metallochemia.

Among the new and fascinating people at the factory were the occasional summer apprentices, one of whom would be starting the following Monday. She'd occasionally be one of those responsible, her supervisor told her, for directing the University of Veszprém student during his work as a research assistant. He'd primarily complete more menial tasks around the lab—cleaning and preliminary tests—but he still needed supervision.

While she'd assisted in supervising others in her role—and it wasn't as dreadful as she'd initially imagined—she still felt a flutter of anticipation at the idea of telling another adult what to do.

She felt a different kind of flutter when the apprentice walked into her lab late Monday morning.

From down the hall, she heard a loud, boisterous glissando of a laugh that, strangely, made her want to laugh, too. As they turned the corner into her lab, she rose from her seat to greet the person whose laugh had intrigued her.

He had beautiful eyes. A rugged mustache accentuated his easy grin, its slight crookedness giving him a playfully boyish appearance. Slim cut and stylish, his blue and white plaid shirt contrasted with his complexion, which was darker than she'd ever seen. She knew immediately that he was the source of that long, bellowing chuckle, and she found herself eager to be invited into the joke.

Despite feeling drawn to this man—or, in truth, because of it—she couldn't seem to find the words to introduce herself. Instead, she stood, arms awkwardly dangling at her sides as she flashed an overly wide smile—a reflexive response to the man's charming demeanor. Suddenly, she couldn't remember how to behave normally.

He didn't seem to care, leaning in warmly to shake her hand and introduce himself.

"I am Okpoma," he said. She could hear only a slight accent coloring his crisp, precise Hungarian, and it only made him more intriguing.

She cleared her throat. "Judit Koós," she said.

His smile broad and warm, he remarked, "Ah, you must be the quality control engineer."

Trying her best to remain professional in the face of this fascinating man—a Black man who actually spoke her language!—she
nodded. "You speak Hungarian very beautifully."

He leaned in playfully. "You do, too!"

A laugh, much too loud for the room, escaped her lips involuntarily, and she looked at the floor, a goofy grin spreading across
her face. She suddenly felt overheated.

She felt his gaze lingering on her, so she kept her eyes down,
willing her blush to dissipate.

"I look forward to learning from you," he said, when she finally
raised her head again. He held eye contact for the full length of
the sentence, as though the exchange was the most important
of his day—at least that's how his manner made her feel, which
was a sharp contrast with most visitors to the office she worked
in. She could never imagine him throwing away the end of the
conversation as he rushed, distractedly, down the hallway.

I look forward to learning from you.

The words echoed in her ears, and she would have laughed if
she weren't so flustered by him—what could this man, a university
student who seemed to have it all together, possibly learn from her?
The sentiment felt nice, she had to admit, even if it was doubly intimidating. In reality, she looked forward to learning more from him.

She couldn't figure out what it was about this man that made
him so magnetic.

When he joined the group for a communal lunch that day, she
realized what it was. Smart and funny, Matthew seemed to charm
everyone he met. And that was a lot of people. The factory, as a
whole, was dominated by female employees and, from what Judit
could tell, every single one was irresistibly drawn to him.

"Where are you from?" one girl asked, moony-eyed.

"How many siblings do you have?" another questioned, leaning across the table.

"Why'd you come to Hungary?"

"What's your religion?"

"Do you like it here?"

With each new question, her heart sank—no matter what was asked or who asked it, he offered the same generous charm he'd shown her in her lab. His eyes almost twinkled as he talked, his uninhibited laugh setting off girlish giggles around the table.

As charismatic as he was, he also showed kindness and sincerity. He didn't seem manipulative or smarmy at all—rather, like an incredible, brilliant, caring person, determined to learn more about those around him.

He was open about himself as well, sharing his hardships: how the city where he'd attended secondary school had been under siege and how he'd had to flee from his college town. It was all very exciting and scary, and he told his history with the flair of a master storyteller.

In a way, he reminded her of her father.

She'd heard many times about her family's brush with war, and not only the story—her favorite—of when they had to cower in their Budapest apartment's basement shelter. When she was just a newborn, her father had monitored the radio, listening for news about the advancing Russian front. He'd described the Allies' carpet bombings, nearly a weekly event in Budapest in April 1944, and warplanes he watched in the distance from their home in Szöllőspuszta.

Her father had been strategic. He knew their little haven sat right in the path of the advancing troops. A practical man and longtime farmer, he knew the family would be defenseless and worried for their safety.

Her father had arranged to send the family away so that they may be better protected.

She'd always thought him so brave and wise, guided by an inquisitive kind of spirituality that wasn't tethered to religion as much as it was to justice.

She liked to think of herself as following in his footsteps in some small way, but she lacked his confidence and strength. Fond of saying, "*kicsi a bors de erős*"—the pepper is small, but strong—he'd tried to encourage her to be more confident.

Somehow his words hadn't moved her the way she thought they should, at least not enough to overcome her self-consciousness.

But now, this young man, who was four years younger than her but who had been through so much, inspired her to stand taller and speak more confidently. Or, at least, she wanted to do those things.

She knew it was easier said than done. And, anyway, what did it matter? Someone like Matthew, with his sparkling, inviting personality, could never be interested in her. At any rate, it was just as well. She could barely hold a conversation with him without clamming up.

And yet, he seemed determined to connect with her.

It was a strange feeling. Never popular with men—not especially popular with women either, for that matter—she'd never seen herself as particularly desirable. She was practical above all else. She wore little makeup and a simple hairstyle that looked presentable but didn't require too much effort. Unlike some of the other women at the factory, she found the lab coats to be one of the job's true perks—there was no point in fussing over an outfit nobody could see anyway.

But, with Matthew's attention on her, she found herself taking extra care to style her hair in the mornings, spritzing some hairspray to keep flyaways at bay and digging out her curling iron on occasion, just to give a little boost to the curls that had flattened themselves while she slept. She even picked up a tube of lipstick and, while it felt strange to see herself with apricot-colored lips, she had to admit it made her feel almost sexy.

One day, when she was feeling particularly good about herself, she took a deep breath and made her way to the communal lunchroom. Matthew sat with a few male workers from a different building and a couple of women she knew, and she willed her heartbeat to slow as she took a seat across from him.

"If it's so difficult for you to figure out, I guess I can come help," one of the men said to him. With a gruff tone she hadn't expected, he continued, "but I don't know why this is so hard for you."

Through a mouthful of food, the man on the other side of Matthew chimed in, "He's right, you know. It really isn't that hard."

Judit looked over at Matthew, outraged at their condescension. His face a mask of confidence, he held the first man's gaze and nodded. She would have crumbled at their rudeness, but he seemed unfazed, even unusually stoic. "I'd appreciate your help."

"What's your name again?" the first man continued.

"Okpoma," he replied.

"What kind of name is Okpoma?"

The second man laughed. "How about we just call you Misi. Hungarian names are much simpler—who can remember a weird name like that?"

Without thinking, Judit blurted, "There's no need to change it!"

The entire table went quiet, and all three men, as well as the women, turned to look at her. With eyebrows raised nearly to their hairlines, the men looked so foolish to her that she nearly laughed in spite of herself.

Before she lost her nerve, she continued, "Okpoma is a very nice name." She turned and looked directly at the second man and added, "if you're so smart, you shouldn't have any trouble remembering it."

Her heart hammered inside her chest, and she almost feared they could see it through her blouse. In truth, she was as surprised as they were—she'd never seen herself as particularly bold, but neither could she stand by and allow such an unnecessary, degrading conversation.

The two men picked up their things shortly after the confrontation and left. But Matthew didn't.

Instead, he looked at her in a way she'd never been looked at, by him or anyone else. His gaze was always penetrating—it always made her feel vulnerable in the best way—but that day at lunch, she saw something more.

Shrugging it off, she assumed he was just impressed with her quick thinking. She was, too, actually! Reasoning that it probably wasn't an opening for anything romantic, she took it as an opportunity to get to know him. He was a very interesting person, after all, and it couldn't hurt to make a new friend.

"What do your friends call you," she asked, "here in Hungary?"

"Mamah," he replied.

"Then that's what I'll call you."

His grin spread, wide and genuine, and she couldn't help but smile back. She felt so connected to him, this man she knew so little about. This man from Africa, a continent she'd barely thought about, seemed to stand so much taller than his physical height. This man was handsome and effortlessly stylish, but smart and kind, too.

This was the kind of man she'd prayed for.

Having resolved herself to friendship—surely, he was out of her league—she was surprised when he asked her to have coffee.

While she'd spent a full hour fixing herself up for the date—at least she hoped it was a date—she felt her self-consciousness melt away the moment they sat at the small, round table in the downtown Budapest coffee shop. But it wasn't just her self-consciousness.

It felt as though the entire universe melted away.

Hours passed as they sat, immersed in conversation, and she found herself sipping her coffee as slowly as possible to prolong their time together. He'd lived a fascinating life, she learned, even reading the entire Bible and most of the Koran, simply because he was curious about Islam.

She'd been a devout Catholic for a long time, but she'd never met anybody as curious about religion as she was.

Now, here he sat, not only explaining his own interest in religion but revealing his background as the son of a priest.

Over the next few weeks, they saw each other more and more, the relationship growing increasingly comfortable. It felt like they were made for one another. Judit had dated a few men before, but she'd never experienced anything like this, the two of them so effortlessly attuned, as though they were on the same wavelength. She never felt insecure or defensive, the way she often did, even with her own family, and she found herself sharing vulnerable, intimate experiences with him.

And he reciprocated.

It all seemed too good to be true.

Maybe it was.

Or maybe it wasn't.

Either way, she'd know soon enough. As abruptly as it started, Matthew's apprenticeship ended, bringing with it a new level of uncertainty about the future she'd imagined with him.

Chapter 9

MÜNCHEN

⁓

FOR YEARS, MATTHEW HAD WILLED time
to move more quickly. His life seemed to crawl forward
through secondary school at Port Harcourt, the turbu-
lence of the war years, and finally, his year of immersive Hungarian
in Budapest. With every fiber of his being, he'd wanted to rush
time and get on with his life.

But now, suddenly, life seemed to lurch ahead, unresponsive to
his sudden urge to slow it down.

He'd purchased his flight to Munich—München, as the
Germans called it—before his apprenticeship. During his time at
Metallochemia, he'd spoken frequently about his plans to attend
the Summer Olympics. Unaccustomed to foreign travel, the
Hungarians leaned in, eyes sparkling, when he recounted his plans.

He'd enjoyed talking about his plans with one Hungarian, in
particular.

As he exited the train and flowed into the terminal—a space
that buzzed with the diplomatic possibilities of the Games—he
wished she were here to share the experience.

The city felt electric.

No stranger to immersive, cross-cultural education, Matthew knew what to expect when he arrived in new, unfamiliar cities, but he couldn't have predicted the sense of excitement that permeated the West German city. Having hosted the Games only once before—thirty-six years earlier, when the Nazis used the Olympic spectacle to promote their hateful regime—the country had promised a peaceful event. Germany planned to show the world its new image.

The country was an ideal choice, in a way. Following the previous summer Olympics in Mexico, including the murders of hundreds of student protesters by the government, the success of the German games was even more pressing. Still hoping to recoup the fascist image that lingered several decades after Hitler's demise, Germany wouldn't dream of taking such an action.

Their primary commitment was to welcome everyone with generosity and openness. While security was still present throughout the city, the Germans tamped down their intimidating imagery, replacing the typical guards with unarmed agents. The Munich planning committee had even surveyed citizens to determine the least political color—light blue, as it turned out—and clad the officers in the apparently neutral hue.

But even more than the peaceful setting, more than the Germans' dramatic efforts to reframe their image, what struck Matthew most was the crowd's diversity. He'd never seen anything like it.

Across the city, streams of people wove into and out of one another, some with skin as pale as Judit's, others as dark as his own, and myriad shades in between. He'd been in Hungary for some time, and rarely saw other Africans. In the areas surrounding the

Olympic village, though, Nigerians were everywhere. He'd almost forgotten what it was like to blend in, his complexion a novelty for so many Hungarians, and it felt good to fit in again. Beyond seeing other Africans, he loved the idea of a like-minded crowd. Munich, at least for the moment, was a place for acceptance and curiosity—a celebration of the feats that were possible if you embraced the strengths of those who were different from you.

Inspired by the global village that swarmed around him and buoyed by the thrill of a new relationship, he floated down the streets of Munich in eager anticipation of watching soccer, swimming, and track.

Of course, the sports were only part of the intrigue of his Olympic visit. There were also the new sights, sounds, smells, and traditions of the city and country itself. Drinking them in with fascination, he took many notes of the things he saw.

Always, at every turn, he thought of sharing his experiences with Judit. He grinned at the thought of it, a big, dopey smile that probably made him look a little crazy to the strangers at the coffee shop where he sat, wishing he could share a pastry with her.

His longing for her had prompted him to pick up an extra postcard. While all his Hungarian coworkers had begged him to write to them from his travels, Judit deserved her own card. With more to say than could ever fit on a postcard, he stared at the blank cardstock in front of him. He felt almost afraid to ruin the card's perfect blank slate. Clean and crisp, the crosshatched texture taunted him, the space both tiny and wide open with possibilities.

He wished he could tell her everything—how she'd caught his eye from the very first time they met in her lab that day, how he'd found her awkwardness charming and adorable, and how he couldn't stop thinking about her. He wanted to tell her that he hoped they could travel together and show each other the world. In his fantasy, they commented on the sights they saw in Munich and beyond, learning more about new cities even as they learned more about each other—and, through the others' perspective, more about themselves.

He wanted to tell her all of that.

And he wanted to tell her that he knew without a doubt, especially now that they were apart, that she could be the woman he marries.

But, given that he intended to mail the card by way of Metallochemia—alongside a second card meant for all of their coworkers—he thought better of it. He couldn't be so bold on a message that could be read by anyone, particularly her coworkers. So, forcing himself to keep his note brief and light, he scrawled out a cheerful message—a slightly more intimate version of "wish you were here."

Then, like a secret code meant to remind her of what she meant to him—what she had done for him, even more than just defending him in the cafeteria that day—he signed his name, "Mamah."

His heart beat a little faster when he dropped it in the bright yellow post box. When he thought of her reading the postcard, he thought of her smile first. Her grin was always bright and genuine, welcoming and warm, and her thoughtful spirituality took his breath away.

Beyond friendly and sincere, she was smart—already a chemical engineer, the same professional title he would hold soon enough, and one of so few women engineers in Budapest.

This was a woman he would never grow bored with—someone who truly taught him as much about the world as he taught her.

She was the woman he would spend his life with.

He vowed to tell her when he next saw her.

But, at the moment, Munich demanded his attention.

He felt the urgency—the shift in the air—before he learned what had happened. Suddenly, the Games that had promoted peace and safety turned deadly. He'd seen a group of Nigerians—at least he thought they were Nigerians—huddled together, amid the sudden chaos that had broken out.

"What's happening?" he asked, surprised by the tension that so immediately flooded his voice.

Face grim, one of the men looked up at him—a Yoruba, if he had to guess—and replied, "There's been a terrorist attack."

He just nodded as the world that had bustled with possibility only hours before now transformed into a space of fear. In the immediate aftermath, the man hadn't known any more details. Someone had broken into the Olympic Village. Two people were dead and several more kidnapped.

Within twenty-four hours, the day's events would come into tragic focus. A group of Palestinian militants called Black September had forced their way into the apartments of the Israeli athletes and coaches. Within the hour, two were dead, as the first athletes to encounter the terrorists had attempted to stop the attack before it began.

They were unsuccessful.

Black September's plan was extraordinarily detailed—even eschewing conflict with the Israeli marksmen in one apartment in favor of the wrestling team in the next—and the group of eight abducted nine Israelis. Demanding the release of two hundred imprisoned Palestinians, the terrorists held the athletes and coaches at gunpoint as German officials struggled to find the appropriate course of action. The plot ended in a deadly shootout. The

Olympic announcer who had been covering the events could only gasp, "They're all gone."

But when Matthew had pulled aside that Yoruba man, nobody knew what would become of the incident. Most didn't even know what, exactly, was happening that morning.

At that moment, they only knew that the Games had started off peaceful and turned violent, and the safety they'd all imagined in Munich turned into a fantasy.

It threatened to knock Matthew off his feet.

He'd lived through violence, of course—more than his fair share—but he'd always bracketed those experiences as anomalies. Very much centralized within his home country, this type of senseless, catastrophic violence didn't make sense on the serene landscape of Europe.

But then, he reminded himself, it hadn't made sense in Nigeria either, at least not when he was young.

Over the next few days, as the events were postponed and replaced by a memorial service, Matthew thought a lot about his home country. He'd been eager to flee the violence, moving around the country during his schooling and, eventually, embracing the opportunity to study in Hungary.

He was glad for that. He'd been able to keep himself safe which was more than many Nigerians could say.

But it was eye-opening to see such familiar violence taking place elsewhere. Like the conflict in Nigeria, the Israel-Palestine conflict centered on territory, pitting people who should have held similar interests against one another in the name of the land.

It also centered on religion. As a Nigerian youth, he'd seen people murdering one another over differences that should have been superficial and meaningless, political jockeying over conflicts that weren't easy to solve, but that certainly didn't require the kind of violence that left a string of dead bodies in its wake.

Perhaps the most striking similarity between his experiences in Nigeria and those during the Munich Summer Games laid in the way the violence transformed the atmosphere. In an instant, the magic of the games dissolved, for Matthew and others. The events only ceased for a single day, but when they restarted, things felt heavy and tense.

The bustle of the Olympic crowd that he had enjoyed now felt like a threat, the noisy commotion of the games, a warning siren.

More than ever, he longed to be home, but not, to his surprise, in Nigeria—instead, he wished for his Budapest dormitory. He wouldn't live there again, he knew. With the fading light of summer, he'd left his internship behind. But he longed for the intrigue of his new, growing relationship.

He and Judit had been coy up to that point, subtly flirting and exchanging little teasing remarks and blushing glances—it seemed quite silly when he thought of it that way. But he didn't care—their coffee shop meetings had been some of the deepest conversations he'd had in his life.

As he rode the train back to Veszprém, he played those conversations back in his head, over and over like a new Stevie Wonder album. To him, their relationship felt settled, as though they'd always known one another, but, at the same time, the excitement of a new love vibrated in his chest, elusive and light.

It was difficult to communicate those feelings through letters, and yet, that was the only available mode of communication. While they were only 650 kilometers away, a distance that seemed short when he considered how far he was from his Nigerian home, the distance sometimes seemed insurmountable. And yet, even with the distance, and even with his school and her full-time work—even with the cultural differences that were both challenging and a source of so much fascinating information—he knew in his bones that she was the one.

He'd gotten overwhelmed with school the previous semester and hadn't written as much as usual. With a level of concern that had surprised him, Judit had written to ask if everything was okay. They'd decided then that they would be in a serious relationship and since then had mentioned marriage a few times.

With some difficulty, he did his best to focus on his studies, but his mind was forever drawn back to Judit. Class after class dragged on, an obstacle to his next visit.

Eventually, with a level of nerves he hadn't felt in some time—and that he was not likely to admit to anyone, including himself—the day arrived that he was to board the train and visit Judit, after traveling to Gödöllő to reconnect with Venance, his friend from the preparatory school.

He'd visited her before many times, of course. During the winter break, he'd spent several days with her, their conversations growing more interesting and more animated as their relationship grew stronger, more predictable. He'd introduced her to Venance, and she told him about her sisters and brother.

He wanted to know her family.

Judit's older sister Bori wore glasses but resembled her the most among the siblings, similarly round-faced, though was a darker brunette. Bori was one of the few people who knew about their relationship, and her husband Béla Hajtman invited the couple to their house. Venance accompanied them.

Her family was every bit as warm and welcoming as Venance had been, despite Judit's clear nerves as they made their way to meet them. She'd looked longingly at her sister as she introduced them, and she leaned into the conversation even more than usual, desperate for Bori's approval.

So he wasn't surprised to see Judit's eyes twinkle when Bori asked, a playful note in her voice, "So are you two," she paused, "serious?"

Judit's face lit up and she bit her lip, perhaps trying, unsuccessfully, to hide her smile.

"We are," he said.

And when she turned to him, her grin overtook her face.

Bori smiled, too, an expression he knew would be important to Judit. She badly wanted her family to like him.

He could certainly understand why. Having never met another girl's family, he wasn't sure how these things normally went, but he knew it was important to him, and to Judit, that her family like him.

Bori and Judit went into the kitchen to chat and grab some snacks, leaving the men alone.

Hajtman seemed very curious about Matthew as he looked at the African men seated in front of him. It was clear by his questions that he wondered what life might be like for his sister-in-law if she married Matthew.

"Will Jutka be hated by Africans?" he asked bluntly. "Would she be attacked?"

Matthew tried to paint a positive picture of his country. He emphasized that foreigners are well-liked in Nigeria, many even taking up residence there. He highlighted the good weather and rapid economic development in his country.

Both Hajtman and Bori were impressed by Matthew's command of Hungarian, as well as his intellectual curiosity. He was charming and entertaining. His signature infectious laugh filled up the room with a good ambience.

If he'd been sure of the relationship back when he visited Munich, he knew now, without a doubt, that he wanted to marry her. After months of longing for one another, the time together had been like a cold drink of water on a hot summer day.

This was a woman who embraced everything about him, who encouraged him and valued him and tolerated his flaws. As though their time together was an elixir in his heart, she seemed to grow more beautiful every day, the joy and life spilling out of her until the whole world seemed to sparkle.

So one night, as they sat, snuggled close to one another, he quietly asked her whether he could meet her parents soon.

With her head leaned against his shoulder, he couldn't see her face, yet he felt her smile—that smile that made her absolutely glow. But then something changed. Lifting her head and repositioning herself to face him, she looked serious.

"My dad," she said, her eyes darting between him and the floor. "He will not..."

"What?" he asked. "He can't be that bad!" He laughed at that, as much to break the moment's tension as out of humor.

She chewed her lip and nodded, then took a deep, strained breath in. "I don't know if..." She paused, swatting away a bug that Matthew couldn't quite see. "He's so protective, that's all."

He'd known that Judit sometimes clashed with her family. The youngest sibling, she'd told him more than once that she frequently felt criticized, as though she would always be a child, even as her siblings—even her siblings' children—grew up around her.

Now that he thought about it, she'd been almost strangely quiet on the matter of him meeting her father. He knew that she'd told her siblings. Before they'd come to Budapest to meet Bori and Hajtman, she'd told him that her siblings were excited to meet him.

It hadn't occurred to him that she had been avoiding talking about her parents, but now it seemed clear to him that she was avoiding the introduction.

He knew she was serious about him. Not only was it all over her face—he loved her for that—they'd also discussed it. It had been clear to them both even when he was away, through their letters. Casual, somewhat superficial mentions of marriage had become common in their talk—she'd see a wedding gown in a storefront and dream of wearing it or a friend would get married and she'd wonder when it was her turn.

He knew she had the same vision of the future for them that he had. Something was holding her back. He just had to find out what it was.

Chapter 10

BARTÓK

UNCLE BÉLA WOULD KNOW HOW to help. Or, at least, Judit hoped he would. She hurried down Köbölkút Street toward the Bartók house, sending up a silent prayer that he would have an answer. With Matthew insisting that he meet her parents—and with her full awareness that such a meeting would be disastrous—she'd found herself with no other options.

Then she'd remembered: Uncle Béla had been to Africa! An ambassador for his late father, the famous Hungarian composer, and more recently as President of the Hungarian Unitarian church, he'd traveled much more of the world than most Hungarians were allowed. Those experiences had brought him more than the worldly wisdom he was known for; they'd also made him tolerant—or more precisely, enamored—of other cultures.

He'd know what to do.

He had to.

With the warmth and wisdom characteristic of Uncle Béla, he greeted her at the door. "Jutka," he crooned, his voice smooth as silk, akin to that of a Hollywood actor. Her pet name rang in her ears with joy. It was an endearing name bestowed on her by her family, but even Matthew had taken to calling her Jutka as the two grew closer.

After the requisite small talk, they moved back into the sitting room where she helped herself to a chocolate from the small crystal bowl on the ornate console table.

"You look so happy, Jutka," he remarked.

As if on cue, a wide smile burst onto her lips. She truly was happier than she'd ever been, even as she faced a challenge with no reasonable resolution.

"I am!" she replied with a little laugh. "I met a boy."

His eyes lit up, and he leaned back on the sofa, his thin legs crossed at the knee, coaxing her to say more.

What she had to say next wiped the grin from her face. "Uncle Béla, my parents will not accept him."

With the force of passion pent up inside her, the story poured out. She and Matthew planned to marry. Try as she might, she could not dissuade him from meeting her father, so she had pre-empted their meeting by approaching her father herself. He had a serious and stern demeanor, his face always set in flat lines. Still, he cared deeply for his youngest daughter, and Judit hoped that would be enough to smooth things over.

It had not gone well.

He had, at first, been supportive of his daughter's plans with this man, raising his thick, dark eyebrows in approval. Matthew was a man of God, she'd explained, well-traveled and smart.

It was when she revealed his ethnicity that things had taken a terrible turn.

"If you bring that blackie into this house, I'll kick his ass," her father had yelled, his white hair shifting from the force of his anger.

Furious, she'd stormed out. She was relentless and determined—nobody would stop her from marrying the man she loved.

She'd had a flash to her own childhood. There had been challenges, then, of course—the political turmoil and the violence they'd seen during the revolution—but there had also been such beauty. She'd felt so light back then, the ease of childhood carrying her through the carefree summers in Vereb.

Vereb didn't have much in the way of urban amenities—a rural area where her father was farm manager, the environment was mostly farmland—but she loved to go along with her father. Of all her siblings, it was his Jutka he chose to take with him each summer, staying in the open space during the warmer months. She would pick blackberries for the two to eat together, but he often didn't take the time to join her.

She'd remembered those days fondly, remembered climbing into the horse-driven coach to ride into town for sugar and soda water, her purple dress swaying in the wind.

Along with her little friend Andrea, she spent days basking in the sun, picking blackberries, and eating until their stomachs felt ready to burst with the sweet fruit. Once, as they lay in the short grass in front of the farmhouse, she and Andrea giggled, looking at their deeply tanned, sun-freckled skin.

"I am sun-tanned like a negro!" Judit had laughed to her friend.

Holding up her arm next to Judit's, Andrea had responded, "I am even darker than you are!"

The days had gone on like that, lazy summer hours that spread out forever, the sweet smell of grass mixed with the dusty scent of the barley fields.

It was these trips to Vereb that made her feel so close with her father. She had wanted to feel the same closeness when she introduced him to the man she would marry.

———

When she'd next seen Matthew, she'd tried gently to convince him to let the whole thing go—they could get married without her father's consent, she reasoned.

Matthew just shook his head and let out another one of his disarming laughs, which always seemed to defuse the tension, even as she suspected a layer of frustration lurked beneath. "No, no, no, Jutka, I have to meet him," he countered, still smiling. "At least…" he'd paused then, his gaze drifting from her. "I have to try."

She'd tried to interrupt him—there was no point in pressing the issue with her father. It would only make things worse.

But he'd persisted.

"Please. If I can't convince him, then we'll get married without his consent."

She was unsure of how to respond, whether to throw her arms around his neck, grateful that they could be married without her father's elusive consent, or to console him, saddened by the unfairness of the situation. She just nodded, her mouth drawn in a thin, determined line.

She'd begun to scheme that night, racking her brain for ways to help the situation along. Initially, she hesitated at the thought of telling Uncle Béla, unsure if he would react like her father. Another encounter like the shouting match she'd had with her actual father would be too much for her—if Uncle Béla reacted the same way, it would break her heart.

But eventually, she realized she had no other choice. If she took Matthew to her father, it might irreparably damage her relationship with both men. She wasn't sure her father would actually fight Matthew, nor was she sure what Matthew would do in such a situation, but she would sooner run away and never come back than stick around to find out.

So, with hesitation, she'd decided to ask Uncle Béla. She couldn't remember a time without him. With no children of their own, he and his wife, Aunt Judit, had taken her in as their own, often inviting her over to spend time at their nearby house.

As kind as he was suave, and with mannerisms that spoke of his artful upbringing, Judit marveled at the unique way Uncle Béla saw the world. She'd always been awed by his and Aunt Judit's love of nature. And, in stark contrast, she loved the intricate, expensive details of their home—cut flowers carefully placed around the house, and beautiful, richly stained furniture with hand-carved details.

Uncle Béla had always been a father figure to her—she considered herself fortunate to have two such figures in him and her actual father—now she needed her uncle to help her gain her father's blessing.

Uncle Béla had other ideas. Instead, he offered to be something of a diplomat, paving the way for Matthew's entrance into the Koós home. He seemed genuinely interested in their relationship, never once condemning their plans for intercultural marriage.

It made her heart swell to think of it. Proud to have found such an intelligent, charismatic man, she hadn't realized how much she longed for her family's approval. Of course, she'd already introduced him to her sister, Bori, who had always been a maternal figure in her life. But she found herself excited to introduce Matthew to Uncle Béla.

That excitement turned to anxious anticipation—happy butterflies that fluttered from her stomach to her throat and back again—as she and Matthew made their way to the number seven bus stop. As the couple approached the stop, situated near the family home on Zsombolyai Street, Judit waved expectantly at Uncle Béla, who smiled warmly at them.

"Jutka," he exclaimed, with an enthusiasm that marked the meeting as even more special than Judit had imagined.

"Uncle Béla, this is Mamah."

The older man extended a hand, and Matthew took it, matching Béla's toothy grin. At the sight of them—two of the three most important men in her life—Judit could have jumped up and down with joy. But she kept her wits about her.

"Uncle Béla has been to Nigeria!" she announced, excited to introduce the two to common ground.

"Ah," Matthew replied. "Where did you travel?"

And, with that, the two men set out on a rather intense version of small talk, Matthew with his characteristic charm and Béla with his calm, smooth acuity.

Their conversation flew freely, a witty rap with laughter scattered easily throughout.

It was precisely as Judit had imagined it, and in the very best way. Except, in her fantasy, her father stood beside them.

Uncle Béla must have sensed her ambivalence, because he took her hand and whispered, "He's a good man. Your father will see it, too."

And then, Béla made his way up to the apartment.

Concerned about seeming disrespectful, Matthew had refused Judit's nudges to go up, insisting that they would wait downstairs until Béla had a chance to reassure her father. She appreciated how patient he was being; she just wished it weren't necessary.

A good man, her father wasn't usually hateful or unreasonable. He'd grown up the youngest of eleven children—a trait Judit often related to as the youngest child herself—and was staunchly set in his ways. As infrequently as Hungarians encountered Black people, they married them even less.

After waiting what Judit hoped was long enough for Béla and her father to talk, the couple climbed the stairs to the apartment. Her heart beat ferociously in her chest, as, more than once, she considered whether it was too late to turn back. Perhaps she could beg Matthew to reconsider. Or, if worst came to worst, she could simply refuse to go any further. Of course, she wouldn't really consider doing any of that. She wanted to marry Matthew, and part of marriage—part of being a mature adult—was doing what was right, even when it wasn't easy.

So, with every ounce of her courage, she took Matthew's hand and continued up the stairs. Their shoes clacked on the tan tile landings as they ascended, echoing in a way that felt new and unfamiliar.

In a way, it was new and unfamiliar.

She'd dated other men before, even introduced one or two to her family, but never wanted to marry any of them. At times, she'd even cursed her luck that she'd never found the kind of man she longed for among her countrymen.

Things were never as simple as they should have been, but now she knew why. She'd always been meant to find Matthew.

As a child, she'd longed for the simple existence her parents had enjoyed on the farm in Szöllőspuszta. The vast property was peaceful and quaint, although Judit realized now that it signaled relative wealth, particularly with its grand profile, massive front columns, and servants and horsemen to help her parents run the place.

The name affectionately shorted to Szöllős, their home comprised of two adjacent farmsteads separated by Aradi Road, the path to the largest nearby city, Orosháza, where she was born.

Not even a year old when they'd fled to Budapest, she couldn't remember living there. But her mother had told her of their life in Szöllős, fondly recounting the raspberry bushes and asparagus she'd raised in a sprawling garden behind the home. Judit had loved to envision her mother as a much younger woman, clad in floral dresses with embroidered bib overlays, her wavy blonde hair swept into an effortless chignon.

It all seemed so simple and pure, a story from a fairytale, made even more fantastical by the descriptions of frogs croaking. A frequent visitor, Uncle Béla's father, the great composer Béla Bartók, had even written a famous composition based on the sound of the frogs: "Night Music" was a warm reflection on serene summer nights on her parents' farm. The piece, among others, earned Bartók fame and fortune around the world.

For years, before he emigrated to the United States at the end of his life, the elder Bartók spent time in Szöllős with the Koós family. They would all gather in the home's spacious salon, a grand room with a hulking fireplace and a large Bösendorfer piano that the composer, an accomplished pianist, would sometimes play. That was Judit's favorite image—music flowing through the halls as her family stood to dance to the lilting music, a compliment to the natural sounds beyond the home's walls.

The composer, a pioneer in ethnomusicology, a field akin to musical anthropology, was her grandmother's only brother. They'd remained close, just as her mother had been close to her cousin, Uncle Béla. Judit's mother had remained geographically close to the memory for as long as she could, with her father passing down the role of farm manager to her husband, Judit's father.

Family had always been important.

She kept that thought close to her heart as she took a deep breath and pushed through the apartment's front door, unsure of what might await her.

Whatever Uncle Béla had said apparently calmed her father's nerves—even if it had done nothing for her own. Her parents seemed cold, but mercifully, there was no violence—she wished she could have assumed a peaceful meeting from the start, but her father's warning rang in her ears.

Matthew put on every bit of his ample charm as they chatted, complimenting their home and her mother's dress and asking her father polite questions to show his interest.

Judit simply could not—would not—understand how they could find him anything other than disarmingly charismatic. And yet, she feared the worst, nervously glancing between her parents and Matthew as the group talked, interrupted only by the occasional reassuring nod from Uncle Béla. Her palms clammy and her throat tight, she tried to focus on the conversation as best she could.

When it was over, she walked Matthew to the door, waiting inside to talk with her parents. She'd scarcely made her way back from the front door when her father proclaimed, "There is nothing wrong with this young man."

Her vision went wobbly as relief flooded her body.

But he wasn't done. "Except," he continued, "that he's Black."

Judit opened her mouth to protest, the wave of release morphing almost imperceptibly into a fiery rage. Before she could protest, he looked her in the eye and, in pleading tones, added, "My dear daughter, in Nigeria, they would sell you for a goat!"

It wasn't the reaction she'd hoped for.

And yet, compared to his threat to beat Matthew, she couldn't help but feel that her father's words were softer. His voice seemed less aggressive, less angry.

Matthew had been charming—she knew he would be—and perhaps he'd begun to win over her father, just as he'd won her over. With no shortage of witty remarks, who could help but love him? Mathew hadn't seemed nervous at all in the meeting, in stark contrast to her own pounding heart and clammy palms.

Bolstered by hope, she decided to bet on Matthew's charm. She would simply arrange for her father to spend more time with him. And, she believed, the more they interacted, the less concerned her father would be.

They would sell you for a goat!

When she thought of his comment, she almost felt a wave of embarrassment—how could her father think such a thing? Let alone, say it out loud?

She'd harbored her own prejudices when she first met Matthew, of course. A novelty that was impossible to overstate, she'd simply never interacted with a Black person and had truly known nothing about Africa.

But after just one conversation with Matthew, she'd realized that he was no different than her, not in any way that mattered. He was smart and studious, funny and lighthearted, passionate and driven, and he envisioned their future together in much the same way she did. She could think of no reason, then, that the color of his skin or his African heritage should preclude their long and happy life together.

So, she set about a plan to show her father the Matthew she knew. The baby of the family, she hated being treated as childish.

But those notions about her maturity could be two-sided—she also got a bit more leeway in her decisions, as her family just saw her quirks as Judit being Judit. Using that to her advantage, she was determined to bring Matthew around as much as possible.

She called her sister Aci first. "I'd love to introduce you to Mamah," she'd said. "Could you come over to the family home?"

Aci delightedly accepted, and the five of them—including their parents—had a lovely conversation. When they met at the Zsombolyai Street apartment, there was really no possibility of the family avoiding Matthew. Perhaps if they still lived in Szöllős, her father could have retreated to either of the dining rooms or to the verandah by the garden, but the cozy little apartment afforded no such escape. Matthew charmed Aci—Judit had no doubt he would—and their parents seemed to relax in their demeanor. In spite of himself, her father even laughed at one of Matthew's quips. She was making progress!

Only a week later, she'd asked Matthew to bring Venance and Nyama, a Nigerian student he knew from school. She no longer felt uncomfortable or even particularly fascinated when she spent time with African students—perhaps the same kind of intercultural immersion would do her father well.

Her brother, Berci, joined them for lunch, and they enjoyed a brothy soup their mother had prepared. Complimenting the meal profusely—Judit thought she'd even seen their mother blush a bit—the three students had fit right in with the family.

Though Venance and Nyama didn't speak Hungarian with Matthew's level of precision—in truth, sometimes Judit thought he was more articulate in the language than she—they were strong conversationalists with the same ambition and intelligence as Matthew. And Matthew, in her opinion, wasn't so different from her father.

Perhaps she was imagining it, but she felt the potential for a true bond between Matthew and her father. Matthew and Uncle Béla had, after all, a lovely conversation, and Berci and Aci seemed to like Matthew very much.

Even if it were all in her head, she'd given Matthew the due diligence he'd asked for. She'd not only introduced them but, as cleverly as she could, she'd also arranged for them to spend time together on several more occasions. From Matthew's original request, she'd been skeptical that anything good could come from them meeting, but now she had to admit that she loved seeing her father and her soon-to-be-husband together, talking and laughing, even if the latter were rarer than she preferred.

She told Matthew as much when the topic of marriage next arose. With his characteristic warm grin, he'd pulled her into an embrace and kissed her forehead. She melted into his arms— hoping that feeling of total safety and trust would never fade.

She smiled into his chest, a little giggle escaping, and she heard him exhale a little chuckle, too.

And with that, their future was settled.

Chapter II

THE EMBASSY

⁓

THE SUN'S RAYS SPILLED THROUGH the
window as Matthew awoke that special day in 1973.
The summer's peak felt familiar and comforting.

August 26. He couldn't believe the day had finally arrived—
time had raced forward, like an eager child, over the past few
months.

Later that afternoon, he and Judit would go to Budapest's
British Embassy and promise their lives to one another. It seemed
almost incongruous, waking up to the sun, like he always did—
except, he reminded himself, the morning only *looked* normal. It
would be, in reality, one of the most notable of his life.

When they'd made the arrangements for the simple, intimate
ceremony, he'd wanted to choose a church akin to his father's. He'd
grown up Anglican, his father having worked in the tradition for
years before he was born.

But, having sought out a church to attend when he'd first
arrived, he knew that not a single Anglican church existed in
Budapest. In those early days in the city, he'd chosen to attend

a Baptist church, reasoning that the denomination's traditions differed only slightly from those he grew up with.

He'd liked the church, although he only attended occasionally—once he'd even dragged Venance along with him. They'd gone through the whole service, far from identical to the Anglican traditions he'd grown up with, but better than nothing.

After the service, a man had tapped his friend on the shoulder. "You boys are much too young to be here," he'd said, in a tone that melded confusion and disagreement.

Matthew cocked his head to the side and narrowed his eyes at the man.

With a hint of a smile on the corner of his lips, the man continued, "Shouldn't you be out in the park having fun? Or chasing girls or something?"

Matthew had laughed, hoping the man's comment was a joke, and continued to attend the church periodically. Venance hadn't gone with him again, always busy after they'd gone their separate ways for university.

Once, Matthew and Judit took a short trip together. Just a short train ride from Budapest, Szentendre didn't look so different from other Hungarian cities, at least to Matthew. But Judit, his sweet Jutka, had delighted at the little town's signature rainbow-colored umbrellas, suspended over a quaint street lined with colorful houses.

Both very passionate about the religion they grew up in, the two discussed the details of the wedding. Judit wanted to marry under a Catholic priest in an homage to the songs that brought her so much joy and passion in her youth. Yet, when she saw the pride in Matthew's eyes as he discussed his faith under his father, she couldn't help but notice, too, the solemnity with which he remembered his father could not attend. Judit gladly accepted an Anglican ceremony for their marriage.

Though the scenery had been stunning, it paled in comparison to his bride-to-be. Glowing with happiness, her smile contagious, she'd showered him with affection throughout the trip. He'd learned so much from her—about the country and their engineering work—falling in love with her sincere eagerness to help. Never condescending, she was always cheering him on, grinning with pride and encouragement.

Venance had liked her, too. All of his friends had.

It was just one more sign that they were meant to be together. And so, after the hurdle of her father—a conflict that would dissipate, Judit assured him—they'd invited his friends from Veszprém and other scattered stations around Hungary to join them at their wedding.

The wedding that would take place that afternoon.

He could hardly believe it. Even with their quick engagement, the time seemed to drag, delaying the day they would officially begin their lives together. That day was finally here.

Pulling his black three-piece suit from the rack, his hands shook with anticipation. They'd chosen local formalwear for the wedding, so he donned a crisp white shirt with a stylish, white tie. After buttoning up the vest, he slipped on the jacket and admired himself in the mirror.

He thought he looked pretty sharp. Until he saw her.

She took his breath away.

Her neatly-styled brown hair peeked from under a bridal cap embroidered with a brightly colored traditional Hungarian design, a long veil spilling out behind it and down her lovely back. The gown's sleeve bore a matching motif, offsetting an otherwise simple, white dress. The crowning jewel was her magnificent, glowing smile.

When he first saw her, he thought she was the most beautiful woman in the world.

She hadn't noticed when he approached, her sister Bori fumbling to secure the cap, so he just admired her for the fleeting moment.

And then, it was time.

An Anglican priest, Reverend Bruce Duncan, had travelled from Vienna to wed them with a ceremony that wasn't so different from a Catholic wedding. Except, of course, that it would take place at the British embassy.

They knelt before him as he served communion, the thirty or so guests behind them standing to acknowledge the gravity of the ceremony then filing to the front to accept the host themselves.

Afterwards, the rings were blessed and a song offered—they'd asked Matthew's university friend Tunde to sing, and his rich baritone echoed from the embassy's walls, deep and clear. At the minister's prompting, they recited their sacred vows. Matthew reached over to squeeze Judit's hand. She turned to him, her smile brighter and more radiant than he'd ever seen.

Then, in a whirlwind moment that was much more intense than he'd anticipated, the minister pronounced them man and wife—Mr. and Mrs. Mamah—an unlikely union, perhaps, but one as strong and solid as they'd ever imagined.

He thought of his parents then. An unlikely union in its own right, their marriage arose from very different circumstances than his own.

He'd heard the story many times.

As a young man of only twenty-two, his father had heard about a middle-aged Christian woman with horrible disfiguring lesions.

The terroristic threat of the smallpox plague had claimed her skin and her community. Forced to isolate herself from others, she'd been banished to live deep in the forest where she would die, sick and alone.

His father's heart broke for the woman. When he told his friends that he could not bear to leave her there, they reacted in horror.

"You don't recover from this curse," one friend warned. "So whatever you do is a waste."

But, as his father often recounted, he'd bucked their warnings. "It is my calling to help people," he responded, an uncharacteristic defiance in his voice. "God will not allow me to die."

Armed with only a black Bible, he'd ventured down the forbidden forest trail to the place where only the closest family members dared tread.

The woman lay motionless next to a tree, but when she sensed him approaching, she rose, and he introduced himself. Disfigured and confluent, blisters stretched across her body, rendering her face barely recognizable.

That day, and many days after, he knelt with her, praying and reading passages from the Bible, and bringing her food.

But, ravaged by the disease, her breaths grew shallower until her weakened body succumbed.

The despair, his father told Matthew when he was a teenager, crippled him. He'd called out to God for answers—wondering how He could let this happen in spite of their diligent prayers—but received no fitting answer.

And then, he saw it: a small, flat, red spot on his face. Soon, the marks were everywhere, covering his hands, forearms, and torso. The lesions turned into small blisters next, filled first with clear fluid and later with pus.

Stomach in knots, he knew he had to go the way of the woman he'd tried to help. He knew the forest well, and, with the clothes and food his friends gave him, he trekked down the path, praying for a miracle. But as he grew weaker and incapacitated in the middle of the forest, he began to lose hope. He would die there, just like the woman, alone and afraid.

It was at this point in the story that Matthew had always sat up, his father's eyes coming alive with a glimmer of joy.

As his father often recounted, a group of Christians came to visit him then, their presence doing little to lift his spirits—he'd prayed with the woman, after all, and read her Bible passages. But it hadn't saved her. He was grateful for the food, though, and the company lifted his spirits—particularly that of a small-framed teenage girl.

The girl, who wore a wrapper around her waist topped with a loose-fitting blouse, visited several times a day some days, praying and chatting in Ogbian. Although she had less education than Matthew's father, she was witty and charming, full of enough energy to make up for his somber demeanor.

He dreaded what would come next, but as the scabs formed and fell off, disfiguring the contours of his face, he found that he felt better. Permanently marked with pocks, his face would never look the same.

But he'd been granted what the woman had not—a life.

He intended to use it.

Soon after, he married the girl—that thin, kind, cheerful girl who had remained by his side when he was all alone, isolated in the forest. Sometime after, they'd started a family. Their first two babies had died from unknown illnesses, and Matthew's father had prayed for healthy children and for his faith to survive the gut-wrenching loss.

His prayers were granted when Comfort came along—his older sister—followed not long after by Matthew himself.

When his father told the story, he got a faraway look in his eye. He truly believed God had spoken to him by sending this girl—Matthew's mother—to save him. The events strengthened his faith, which he'd gratefully passed on to Matthew and his sisters.

Matthew saw that same faith when he looked at Judit, there next to him, kneeling at the altar on their wedding day.

"Mamah," she said now, rocking her shoulder against his arm. "Are you happy?" The phrase mimicked concern, but Judit didn't look concerned at all—in truth, she'd worn an enormous smile all day, her eyes brimming with joy and light.

He smiled at her and gave a little wink, which she answered with a soft laugh.

And then it was done. They made their way out of the embassy building, the small, intimate crowd overwhelming them with a flurry of activity. On the embassy's landing, the snap, chk-chk-chk, snap of cameras flashing and film advancing was like music, and he grinned at his wife as they looked this way and that, posing as their friends and family commemorated the day.

From the embassy, they'd gone to a professional photographer—Judit had wanted that, and he went along, her excitement contagious. They'd arranged to have Berci take them there. Decorated with sprigs of lilies and greenery, his small, box-shaped Lada waited at the curb, and they all but bounded to the vehicle, laughing to themselves as they went.

The photo session gave way to a small reception at the Zsombolyai Street apartment. Taking Judit's hand in his, he climbed the stairs to the apartment, recalling with wonder the nerves they'd both felt when he came to meet her father only a few months earlier. The sound of joviality seeped through the apartment door and, when they entered the space, cheers erupted. Judit laughed, melodious and light, and he wrapped his hand around the small of her back as she gazed up at him, that same vibrant grin spread wide across her beautiful face.

A cramped space—no more than a hundred square meters—the thirty-or-so guests filled the apartment to capacity. He glanced around the room, forming a mental map of their guests—Venance grinned and waved from a corner of the living room where he and Tunde were chatting, Bori grinned in their direction, and Uncle Béla lifted a glass to toast. And then, her father was there, next to them, the shimmer in his eyes unmistakable.

"Jutka." He embraced his daughter before stepping back, holding her shoulders. "You look beautiful, my dear."

Then, her father turned to him, extending his hand toward Matthew. He took it, surprised by the strength of his father-in-law's grip. Before he could think of what to say, Albert filled the gap. "If you are my daughter's husband," he said, "then you are my son."

He felt Judit's eyes on him, wide and delighted, but he held his father-in-law's gaze and nodded. "Thank you," he answered.

The relief of the conversation catapulted them around the apartment, as they nearly floated through the reception. They greeted Nyama and Uncle Béla first—the two men had officially witnessed the marriage by signing the certificate. Nyama chatted easily with Venance and Adams, and Reverend Duncan stood close by. Uncle Béla stood nearer the piano—his father's old instrument—which was strewn with vases and other trinkets, a testament to its disuse over the past few decades.

And, of course, they greeted each of Judit's siblings, the women hugging and swooning over her dress, her cap, and her veil.

The night grew more and more festive as guests toasted the couple and danced, and, as the early evening turned to night, the entire room burst into song. Not just any songs, but a series of Hungarian Notas, popular folk songs delivered in a traditional gypsy style.

"*Szeretni, szeretni, szerettelek,*" they sang, a verse meaning "to love, to love, I've loved you," that, while tender, was sung with such exuberance, he had to laugh. "*Feleségül elvenni mégse mertelek.*"

At that, he grinned at her. "To take you as my wife," it meant, "I never dared."

But he had dared. And she, too, had dared to take him as her husband.

The boisterous song was like a wave, washing over the room as men swung their glasses high and women tittered with laughter. And then, with a round of thunderous applause, the song—and the night—were over. The couple bid their farewells and descended the staircase, bound for their bridal suite.

Soon after, they would sublet an apartment until Matthew had to go back to Veszprém to finish school. But, for that moment, there was no energy to worry about such things. Berci drove them to the hotel as Matthew and his wife collapsed into one another, exhausted and giddy, Judit's arm wrapped around his own and her head heavy on his shoulder.

He couldn't remember a time when he was this happy.

And yet, he'd overheard a comment from the priest, an idea he wished he could push from his mind. "There is nothing wrong with people from different countries getting married," he'd said to Judit's sister. "It will, however, be difficult for the children. They won't belong anywhere."

They would have to prove the man wrong, he guessed. And, he hoped, they'd know soon enough.

Chapter 12

A COUPLE OF BREATHS

⁓

THE LARGER HER BELLY GREW, the wearier Judit became—and not just physically. Strangers, it seemed, loved to comment on her pregnancy.

"Oh!" strangers would exclaim. "You must be due soon!"

Some simply cried, "Wow!" or, with a smile and a gasp, "My God!"

"You're huge!" was her least favorite of all, but it happened to be true. Her family had never seen a pregnant woman as large as Judit, and, while she grew tired of hearing about her size, she mostly just grew tired. The extra weight was a lot to carry around!

Very shortly after the wedding, she'd noticed a change in her body, and the doctor had glowingly informed her that she would soon be a mother. For so long, she'd felt lost, as though wandering through life without a purpose. Now, married with a baby on the way, she could see what God intended for her—now a little family of three.

Except, after she felt the quickening—a strange feeling she'd heard described, but that she never quite understood until she felt the fluttery, unsettled feeling deep in her abdomen—she'd gone for a check-up. Their Indonesian doctor at the Tétényi Street Hospital had looked up from her stomach with a big grin.

"Twins!" he'd exclaimed, in accented Hungarian.

It seemed there would be more than three Mamahs. There would be four.

Elated at the opportunity to so quickly grow her family, she'd heaved in delight.

But the larger the babies grew inside her—the larger she grew—the more that excitement mixed with fear. She'd always known she wanted to be a mother, but now, staring down the prospect of motherhood, she found that worry became a part of her everyday life. So many things could go wrong.

Her family knew this well. A dangerous and tense situation, her own birth story had always seemed to her exciting—thrilling, even. She found that she enjoyed the story less the further her own pregnancy advanced. As an expectant mother, the story nagged at her like never before.

The snow had fallen heavily, the story went, enveloping the village in white. In Szöllős, February often draped the hillsides in thick layers of powdery flakes, but that day brought a distinct challenge. Baby Judit was coming—and fast.

Her mother had felt the telltale cramping in her abdomen, a sensation not so different from the four previous deliveries, but this time they lived in a countryside estate—a far cry from the town of Gyula where they'd lived before. In stark contrast to Gyula's modern amenities, Szöllős didn't even have a pharmacy, let alone hospitals, doctors, nurses, or midwives.

It was a difficult place to be nine months pregnant.

And yet, there they were, the snow hardening to ice and Baby

Judit refusing to wait. So her mother had grabbed her warm, brown fur coat and climbed into the coach. Led by the Murakoz horses with their brown, muscular bodies and signature white-centered faces, her mother hadn't been sure about traveling through the snow. But the horses were strong native breeds and the coachmen were experienced, and she was grateful for the nest of warm blankets that had been placed there for her. At least, she reassured herself, there were two coaches. Should one break down on the hour-long ride—and she prayed it wouldn't—they would have a backup.

When Judit thought of her mother climbing into that coach, belly cramping and huge, it made her chest tight. She'd found the story charming as a child. Looking down at her own swollen abdomen, she couldn't believe it. What if she'd arrived before they reached the town? Would the coachman have delivered her? Judit couldn't imagine it—she wouldn't. Women died that way. Babies, too.

Fortunately for both Baby Judit and her mother, they'd made it to Orosháza, turning down the wide gravel pathway of Aradi Road where they navigated the icy, pitted trail as best they could. Her mother recounted the beauty she'd seen—between contractions—as the white expanse stretched before her, offsetting a lazy train that plumed steam into the air next to the coach.

As beautiful as she'd found the train, more beautiful were the houses and apartment complexes that welcomed Judit's mother to town. The Lutheran church's beige tower rose high over its bronze roof, beckoning them to enter. With the coachmen at her side, Judit's mother had waddled into a private room with a crib, the nurse ready and waiting.

Thankfully, the delivery itself had gone smoothly. The two had overcome the journey, and Judit had made her triumphant, noisy entrance into the world, her head full of hair and her eyes deep brown like everyone in the family except her mother.

As Judit reflected on the difficult journey her mother had made to bring her into the world, she marveled at her mother's strength. Her parents had decided on her name in advance. Judit, she would be called. It was her mother who first called her Jutka, the name's diminutive form. Thinking of it now, she vowed to settle on her babies' names well in advance—thinking of her mother cooing her name at her tiny, swaddled figure was one of her favorite parts of the story, and she wanted that for her children, too.

Thinking of it, she ran her hand over her distended naval and felt a flutter of movement. She grinned. "Behave in there, *kis bogaraim*," she whispered with a little giggle.

Her mother's story had made her seem so calm, so completely centered, even in a life-changing and dangerous moment. Of course, her mother had given birth several times before Judit, so she knew what to expect.

Judit had gathered all of the information she could from other mothers she knew, but she still wasn't sure how the birth would go. While she hoped for her own strength, she had no idea how to prepare herself—no idea how she would react when it was time to deliver.

The thought made her breath catch in her throat.

So, as her body grew, she and Matthew moved from their little sublet in the heart of Budapest to the family home on Zsombolyai Street.

Otherwise, she tried to carry on as usual. Matthew soon returned to Veszprém for school, and she kept working at Metallochemia as long as she could.

By April, fatigue replaced the pregnancy's earlier waves of nausea. She began her maternity leave, then, a declaration that sent a jolt of excitement and nerves through her body—motherhood was coming, ready or not.

Most days, she thought she was ready.

That was a very good thing as the days and weeks flew forward, piling up as her belly grew.

And then, one night in May, a shock of pain pulsed through her body.

She thought it was just a cramp at first. As the weeks had progressed, her body had become less and less predictable. She rose to get a glass of water, assuring herself it was just a false alarm—she was still two weeks early, after all. Matthew was still away at school. But the pains continued until they threatened to bring her to her knees.

As dawn approached, she prayed the babies might wait—that she could hold off the way her mother had for that long trip into town. She could call Matthew then.

Instead, she journeyed into the dark of night, her mother at her side, and checked into the maternity ward as the pains grew stronger and more frequent until, finally, it was time to push.

Those moments felt like an eternity, her body ripping itself apart in a tangle of blood and nausea and screaming-hot pain. But as the clock struck four, her labor was greeted with a faint, raspy cry.

The room seemed to explode. An infant nurse, an on-call doctor, and what felt like dozens of others descended on the room, some smiling, some serious.

Where was her boy?

He was here, she knew. She'd heard him. But somehow, too, she felt him. Like she would never be alone again, at least not in the way she had been before.

And then a nurse held him up, and she saw his beautiful, sweet, delicate face.

Time stopped.

She was a mother.

His mother.

And he was her son.

She worried her heart might explode at the thought of this perfect, little bean of a child, a Mamah and a Koós, hers and Matthew's—theirs—and she thought she might drown in pure joy.

"Ready for one more?" the nurse said.

And then she remembered. She wasn't done. Not even close. Gasping for a moment of rest, she tried to steel herself. She'd forgotten about the pain but, in a flash, it swept over her again. And just as she had before, she bore down against it, the world going quiet for a moment until, in a second explosion of sound, light, and movement, the second boy emerged.

She had nothing left to give, and yet, she knew that was her life now—she would give what she could and, when she couldn't give anymore, she would find a way to give anyway. It was her calling—her fulfillment.

With that thought in mind, she conjured her last bit of strength and lifted her head just enough to see.

This little one looked like his father.

Like Matthew.

She felt a tear on her cheek. Or, perhaps it was a drop of sweat. She didn't know for sure—she didn't know anything for sure. She only knew she'd found the meaning that had eluded her for so long.

When the nurse held the tiny, gooey, little one up to her, she touched his perfect, squirmy foot with its perfect, wiggly, impossibly tiny toes, and she let out a little laugh.

"Hello, *kisfiam*," she whispered. The greeting startled her, reminding her that these perfect little gifts didn't yet have names. Hours—a lifetime, it seemed—earlier, she'd placed a slip of paper into the pocket of her gown. She retrieved it now for her sons and, just as her mother had done years ago for her, she told the world who they would be.

Ayibatonye and Obebiedoni.

The first meant "God's will" in Matthew's native Ijaw. The second meant "good journey" in Ogbian, the language a nod to the baby's grandmother.

Tonye and Obibi, the two would be called, both healthy and much larger than expected. She chuckled a bit at the nurses' exclamations—"This one is 3.5 kilograms! Such a big boy!" She'd heard the same before, when the two were still in her womb. But now, she thanked God that they'd come into the world happy, healthy, and, at least by the standards of newborn twins, chubby. In fact, they'd weighed in at about six kilograms, combined!

Their father would be so proud.

Their father.

The thought of her sweet Matthew as a father made her heart swell—everything made her heart swell, it seemed—and when she awoke to find him sitting near her bed, cradling one tiny little swaddled nugget, the joy threatened to overwhelm her.

Within a few days, the boys became such a normal part of her life that she couldn't imagine a time before them. The first few days became the first few weeks—quickly now, too quickly—and those weeks soon gave way to months.

Though similar in appearance, with light brown skin and large, black curls framing their faces, they'd developed their own little personalities, each distinct from the other. Tonye was jumpy and frightened easily. When Judit suddenly bent over his bed, he startled. Obibi was more jovial and often got more animated and ecstatic when strangers looked at him. Obibi liked the pacifier more than Tonye did.

She'd placed the two cribs next to each other, standing so she could play with both simultaneously. She moved her hands in different directions, counting, and the boys' eyes followed her fingers. She placed little rubber animals at the ledge where the two cribs touched and watched as their chunky arms moved up and down, legs kicking and giggles filling the room.

But then Obibi began to change.

No longer content to sleep in his crib, he rarely stopped fussing, no matter what she did. He'd been such a happy baby. With the familiar sense of worry like a boulder on her chest, she bundled him up and took him to Dr. Judit Zakariás.

The doctor simply sent them to an otologist who cleaned out the baby's ear and packed it with cotton wool.

And with that, Judit tamped down her concern. It was funny, in a way, how she'd fretted over such a minor issue. Obibi would be fine. All babies fussed. She'd truly worried for nothing.

As fall turned to winter, she felt herself approaching the coming holiday with the giddiness of a child. Christmas had always been her favorite—and a favorite of her family—and, already eight months old, the boys could really enjoy being spoiled by the family. She helped them to polish their little shoes on December 6, setting them out for Mikulás—the Hungarian name for Santa—explaining to baby Tonye and little Obibi that they would wake to find them stuffed with goodies.

The next morning, the boys ransacked their big bouquet of szaloncukor and assorted chocolates, delighting in the two brightly wrapped gifts. Tonye ripped the paper off first, staring not at the gift, but at the celebratory picture on the box. Everyone laughed then, and Judit's chest swelled with pride. Later, she'd tried to sketch his darling, wonder-filled face. She should have known it was a fool's errand—both boys were too beautiful to capture by portrait, least of all with her amateur efforts.

But as the days passed, dread crept into her throat.

Her father came down with the flu the morning of Christmas Eve, the day "little Jesus"—and the children's presents—would arrive. Their eyes reflecting the glistening szaloncukor candy wrappers on the tree, the boys looked so different from one another. Judit compared their size with a familiar, nagging worry. With each passing day, Tonye's spirited strength revealed Obibi's weakness.

Obibi awoke the next day with a high fever. A new tooth emerged at the lower, left side of his little gums, and she reassured herself that the tooth must have caused the fever. But as his forehead grew hotter, he developed nasal discharge. He looked tiny and frail as he struggled to breathe, and Judit tried nose drops, rocking him and soothing him, fear spreading through her gut like an icy river.

And then Obibi couldn't drink his tea.

Despite sucking at the bottle fervently, he seemed unable to swallow.

She could no longer reassure herself.

That night, Dr. Zakariás came for a house call, common at that time, administering pipolphen and calcium and urging her to take the pitiful little boy to the László Hospital if he didn't improve.

Only a few hours later, Judit took the admission slip the doctor had left behind, wrapped the little one in warm blankets, and shushed the squalling infant as he wheezed and choked.

"It's probably influenza," Dr. Edit Garami said, flashing Judit a reassuring smile. "He'll be fine in a few days."

But by December 29, he'd only gotten worse.

He was admitted to laryngology with a barking cough. "Croup," the doctor had said then. He was placed under a steam tent for two days and intubated. Four days after the intubation tube was removed, his dyspnea continued.

With no options remaining, the doctors recommended a tracheotomy.

Judit thought her heart might burst at the thought. This tiny, frail, innocent baby—a baby she could not protect, could not save—was treated with a small incision at the base of his throat.

If she could have gone in his stead, she would have.

She didn't know then, but the child, her sweet, sweet boy, had only a fifty-percent chance of survival.

Around her, others seemed to blame themselves. Her father had smoked two packs of cigarettes every day for as long as she could remember. Now, after a nurse confirmed that this smoking may have contributed to the baby's condition, he'd quit cold turkey. Matthew, too, wondered what he could have done.

But none of their guilt could compare to her own.

She knew it was silly. She'd done nothing wrong, and she knew there was nothing more she could have done. None of this was her fault. And yet, she couldn't shake the sense of guilt, the instinct that told her she needed to save her child.

As if mocking the quickness with which the boys' first months had passed, the days now plodded along, dragging their feet as her little one struggled in his hospital crib. She felt as though she would never again see the sun, never again laugh or sing.

She worried that she wouldn't survive. That Matthew wouldn't survive. That they couldn't, as a family, endure what was to come.

Tonye, healthy and thriving, still needed care. She and Matthew moved through the motions of nursing, playing with him, and tending to his needs. But their hearts were split in two—half went to their healthy child, and half to the sick.

On January 8, they visited with the doctor. The visits were as common as they were terrifying, and she and Matthew clung to each other's hands, finding strength in one another though neither had it to give.

But that day, the news was good.

Obibi's breathing had improved, his respiratory rate nearing normal ranges.

"Just a touch of diarrhea," the doctor commented, and Judit felt a smile spread across her face.

She knew how to handle diarrhea!

Breathing a sigh of relief, she brought pureed apples to the hospital, elated when he ate it. His voice was raspy, as his throat wound hadn't yet healed, but when his father clowned around with him, he laughed—her baby had laughed!

She'd feared she would never hear the music of his giggle again.

The tiny, sickly boy even stuck out his tongue at her.

And then, she knew. He would be okay.

The horror was over. Tucking a wad of forints discretely in an envelope, she placed the small token of gratitude on the doctor's desk and wrapped the little one, taking him home again, not quite a year from the time she'd first bundled the two babies and brought them back to the house on Zsombolyai Street.

They'd survived.

Their little family of four was whole, safe, and joyful. And, finally, she could look ahead to what the future had in store.

Chapter 13

MANCUNIANS

～～

H E'D AIMED HIGH AND SHOT high. Having graduated from university the spring before, in October 1975, Matthew knew he had more than earned his family's pride. And, as the hope of his people, he had to fulfill his obligation.

He had to go home.

Dutifully and with a pang of sorrow, he kissed Judit and the boys goodbye and made his way to Nigeria. Every Nigerian university graduate younger than thirty-one was required to complete their National Youth Service Corp experience. For his part, he would work in the town of Ughelli.

The real sacrifice was leaving his family behind. By the time he left, his wife's belly was round again.

Six months pregnant when he left for Nigeria, he knew she'd handle his absence as best she could, but it weighed heavy on his heart to travel so far only a few months before his child would come into the world.

He knew how much he'd miss.

When the twins were born, he had been away, too. He'd been finishing his degree in Veszprém then, so his father-in-law had called with the news. As the dormitory porter told Matthew later, he'd initially turned the new grandfather away—with dawn barely on the horizon, it was too early for phone calls.

But mercifully, his father-in-law had insisted, telling the porter to wake him.

He'd just become the father of two beautiful, healthy boys.

In an instant, his entire world had changed.

At that time, he hadn't really known how to be a father, so he'd done all he could think to do. Throwing on a pair of pants, he scrambled to gather his things. He knew he looked a mess, bleary-eyed from too little sleep as he tossed essentials into his bag.

"Mamah has become a papa!" his roommate had joked.

After that, everything was a blur. For the first few days, they'd spent their time in the hospital. Little balconies extended off the building, and he and Judit had enjoyed the lush greenery and fresh air as friends and family came to celebrate little Tonye and Obibi. Some friends made their voices high-pitched and childlike, whispering greetings to the infants: "Hello, gorgeous little fairies!" and "Oh, look at them!" and "How beautiful!" Others simply smiled.

His chest swelled with each new bit of praise.

They were beautiful. With their deep brown eyes and loose ringlets of black hair, they were chubby and happy and perfect. Their skin tone was closer to Judit's than his own. Still, the two boys were the perfect combination of the two of them, and he loved cradling them in his arms, smelling their soft little heads.

He'd hated being away when they were born, but even more, he hated the distraction of finishing school while they struggled to get Obibi healthy.

And now, yet again, he was away.

This time, there would be no quick trip to Budapest. Given the difficulties of communication between Hungary and Nigeria, there likely wouldn't even be a phone call.

To distract himself, he'd buckled down with his work, even making a new friend, Stevie, in Ughelli. Both were engineers—Matthew, chemical, and Stevie, mechanical—who had trained in Europe and married Europeans.

And yet, no matter how he tried to focus on work and friends, he found his heart was always with Judit, nearly five thousand kilometers away. It felt strange, to be both in his home country and homesick for his family.

But true accomplishment was never easy. Often, it required deep, difficult sacrifices—being away from his wife as she prepared to bring their children into the world certainly qualified.

So he tried to focus on the joy he felt—and not the pain of longing—when he received the letter in January.

He had a daughter.

Ebinimi, her name meaning "it is good" in Matthew's native Ijaw language, was happy and healthy.

The labor had been faster and easier than with the boys, his wife wrote. He could almost hear her voice in the letter, recounting the details—she'd called the nurse around two o'clock in the afternoon, worried that the contractions had begun when the doctor wasn't yet there. Instructed not to push, she'd tried to breathe through the pain, her urge to deliver growing stronger and stronger.

And so, she wrote, when the doctor arrived, she'd given one strong push and brought the big baby girl into the world.

Two sons and a daughter.

They'd prayed for this outcome. For Judit, a girl would complete their little family. They agreed the children would grow up healthier being of mixed gender.

They were a family of five.

Now more than ever, Matthew felt the pressure to provide for his family.

And then, one day on the bus, he opened the paper and saw his name.

Since he was a teenager, he'd habitually read the paper any chance he got. On the train, during school breaks, and even in the hospital when Judit and the babies napped—he always had at least one paper with him.

But he'd never seen his name.

His heart skipped a beat and a wide grin spread across his face— he'd been awarded the coveted Federal Scholarship, an honor that would allow him to earn a Ph.D. at Manchester University.

He'd gotten similar offers before. In January, he'd received a scholarship from Edinburgh University, an offer that went along with his acceptance to the graduate program in chemical engineering. But, with his obligation to complete his youth service, he'd had to decline.

The Federal Scholarship, though, was an opportunity of a lifetime. With a growing family, he needed something like this—a tangible way to fulfill his dreams of aiming high and shooting high, and one that would provide economic stability, and possibly even wealth, to his family.

So, although he dreamed of one day moving his whole family home to Nigeria, for now, that dream would have to wait. His training was to take place in Manchester. As soon as he finished his time in Nigeria, he would register for his graduate training in England. The family would become Mancunians.

Perhaps it was just as well. Nigeria wasn't unstable—at least, it wasn't anywhere close to the collapse he'd seen as a younger man—but things were shifting.

The country had added seven new states, bringing the total to nineteen. While some had hoped that an upland Port Harcourt State and a riverine Rivers State would be the outcome, Matthew found the demand for independent jurisdiction among the riverine regions deeply upsetting. His own village remained unchanged and without advancement, even now, nearly a decade after he'd first hoped the government might bring electricity and running water to the town.

Despite the relative lack of progress in his home village, the country entered a new moment of tumult. He'd turned on the radio one afternoon to find that Nigerian politics seemed to be playing on a loop. Just ten days after the new states were announced, President General Murtala Muhammed was dead, ambushed by assassins.

It was the assassin's voice he heard on the radio that day. "I bring you good tidings," he said, his voice a chilling calm. "Murtala Muhammed's deficiency has been detected. His government is now overthrown by the young revolutionaries."

It was an achingly familiar moment that brought back an unsettling flood of grief. Unstable again, his country seemed constantly on the brink of overthrow.

He'd seen that it wasn't only his country that struggled with such strife—his Olympic experience proved that, and he knew, too, from Judit, that Hungary had born its own share of political upheaval.

Resolved, he turned his mind to the family's next move. They'd had so little time together as a family, and he longed to be nearer to them. The boys were growing, and his daughter would be experiencing so many new milestones soon.

He strolled onto the University of Manchester campus in January 1977 and met his professor for the first time. An elderly man with snow-white hair, he eagerly welcomed Matthew, who quickly plunged into the work of a doctoral student.

He counted the days until his family could join him in Manchester. To his surprise, the time passed quickly. Finally, in March, he held his baby girl in his arms. She wasn't so small anymore. The boys, too, had grown so much. As excited as the boys had been about the flight—they babbled about it throughout the three-hour train ride from the airport to their little apartment—they were even happier to see him.

It didn't take long for the family to settle in—a very good thing, considering the changes on the horizon. It wasn't only Matthew who would begin school—the boys had grown so much during his time away. Already prepared for kindergarten, the twins looked forward to starting school just like their father. Apu, they called him, the Hungarian word for Daddy.

They hadn't been in Manchester long when he walked to their school to sign them up, eager to have them registered and accepted, although they wouldn't start until the next fall. Since the school was near enough to the apartment that they could walk, Judit would take them through the yard of the school, sometimes returning with amusing stories about their antics. Obibi, now shortened to Obi, had once refused to leave the schoolyard, fascinated by a soccer game he'd seen there, and Tonye acted silly whenever they encountered Sharon, the neighbor girl.

They were both so full of energy. He sensed Judit's relief when they started school—when she was at home with the kids, she struggled to keep them under control. She often seemed exhausted by the end of the day.

Matthew, too, felt exhausted. Usually in the computer room, the screens reflecting on his glasses, he worked long after others had gone home. He took his job in the Department of Chemical Engineering very seriously. It was a prestigious job—an assistant at the University of Manchester Institute of Science and Technology. He'd learned long ago that a surefire way to distinguish himself from other workers was to maintain incredibly high standards—even if it meant working well into the night.

But they made it work. When he didn't arrive home until ten or eleven at night, the kids sometimes stayed up to greet their Apu, so he could help bathe them, dress them, and put them to bed. They could sleep late, after all, and it was more important for them to spend time with their father. On Sundays, he worked at home, his little cassette player keeping him company. Sometimes he worked in bed.

Judit teased that he even worked in his dreams. If that was the case—if that was what it took to set himself apart from the others—then so be it. He was determined to finish his program at the top of his class.

Still, always, Nigeria called him home.

A letter arrived one day from his sister. Sick with some unnamed malady, his mother needed medications, and Comfort hoped he might send money. She reported that their mother had lost a lot of weight and had some sort of hearing problem. He read the letter over several times, but his sister's words were vague—frustratingly so. With no idea which medications their mother needed, or even if those prescriptions would help, he wired his sister money. He'd always been the hope of the family—his success was their pride.

When he finally finished his thesis—a feat that required him to buy a typewriter, an expensive but necessary purchase—they would be even prouder. Judit had continued to write to them with updates, sometimes even sending them gifts, but they didn't often write back.

He hoped they were happy. As the years passed, he found that more and more likely. Nigeria finally settled back into civil rule, choosing Shehu Shagari—a man of small stature who wore a tall, intricately woven kufi—as its first democratically elected President. There was a sense of optimism returning to the country like a warm, comforting blanket. Things had been bad before, and they'd always recovered. Now, there was a real sense that the people's economic situation would substantially improve.

It was like a sign, an invitation to return home. He could tell his family—in person—about all he'd accomplished. He could introduce his mother and father to his wife and children.

Soon there was another sign. Shortly after he defended his Ph.D. thesis, he received an interview invitation from Shell International. Months later, shortly after Margaret Thatcher began her tenure as Prime Minister, they left Manchester for a short visit to Hungary.

Then the family was bound for Nigeria. They were bound for home.

Chapter 14

GARDEN CITY

MANCHESTER WAS STRANGE. Everywhere she went, new unfamiliar things awaited her. She'd expected to be jolted by the cultural differences—the uncanny punch of new tastes and sights— but the changes were often subtle, unremarkable.

Her English tutor chuckled at her confusion when she'd marveled at the strange choices of the language. People said, "I'm sorry," not only as an apology, but as a gesture of sympathy.

"English can certainly be a bit odd!" Mrs. Power said.

Judit agreed.

Unlike Hungarian, with its predictable, phonetic pronunciations, English overflowed with special rules and exceptions that made her eyebrows scrunch beneath the round frames of her glasses. It was a strange adjustment, particularly all the pronouns. In Hungarian, the same pronoun is used for everyone, but English uses distinct words for each gender.

Mrs. Power came twice a week, and she often pointed out that Judit had mispronounced some word or another.

"We don't voice the 'u' in 'because,'" she said one day. Other days, she corrected her substitution of the "w" sound with a "v" or the "th" sound with an "s".

These were picky things, as far as Judit was concerned—just part of her accent.

Mrs. Power mispronounced things, too—Judit's name, in particular. "In Hungary," Judit had explained, "the 'J' always sounds like yuh. Yudit."

"Oh, I beg your pardon!" the older woman replied.

Judit just shrugged. In truth, she didn't mind people pronouncing her name differently outside of Hungary. She adjusted to many things about Manchester. She learned where to find ingredients and spices similar to those back home, as well as which ones made good substitutes. On occasion, she received a package from Bori containing sweets for the family and true Hungarian paprika. Twice, Uncle Béla came to visit and entertained the children long enough for Judit to rest and enjoy his presence.

Their time in Manchester had, unfortunately, coincided with "the Winter of Discontent," a time marked by strikes across the public and private sectors. The result had been a series of price hikes, coupled with a lack of access to basic needs, all made even more difficult by the fact that Matthew had nearly constant work.

In their last days in Manchester, England had just begun to rebuild after a long period of unrest and worker uprising. Though trash still lay in the streets and grocery prices remained inflated, a sense of peace had finally returned to blanket the country.

Her time with Mrs. Power flew by and, when the time came to leave Manchester, she gathered the children and strapped the big hand luggage across her shoulder.

Before traveling to Nigeria to settle permanently in their new home, the family spent some time back home in Budapest. Judit wanted to spend a few months with her family, but she also wanted the boys to experience a European elementary school—even if only for a semester.

Matthew travelled first to make arrangements for the family's arrival, and finally, Judit and the children made their way to the Zurich airport to board a flight to Nigeria.

The children settled into the flight even more quickly than she did. Shy at first, they were delighted when the stewardess gave them each a little Swissair figurine. Judit thought it said a lot about the crew that they took such care with her children, and they were a great help for the rest of the very long flight.

As they ascended toward the heavens, she leaned across Ebinimi to look through the window. She remembered being told by relatives that mountains could be seen approaching Africa. All she saw were clouds.

As they came closer to her new home, a striped yellow carpet came into view. It was the desert, she eventually realized, molded into waves by the wind.

Two hours later, they landed at the Murtala Muhammed Airport in Lagos. As the plane descended through the black of night, she realized she needed to move quickly to gather up the children and the sweaters, bags, and toys seemed to have multiplied during their hours in the air.

They shuffled to the front of the plane and onto the tarmac, the hot, damp breeze sucking the air from her lungs for a moment.

And then they were in Africa.

In Hungary, she'd once visited a greenhouse with palm trees. With their lush tops and wrinkly trunks, they were a rare and exotic sight she'd found fascinating. But here, they were everywhere, with no glass ceiling in sight. The bright fluorescent lighting reflected on the gray tile floor, shining brightly as Judit and her children weaved around the airport's thick white columns. A whirlwind of brightly-colored wrap-skirts and tunics entered Judit's vision from every corner. Things moved quickly in every direction as she attempted to steer her own family.

"Madam!" a young dark-skinned man exclaimed. His accent was thick—so thick it was difficult to understand—but the man reminded her that she'd see her husband soon, and her heart skipped in anticipation.

Then it skipped in fear.

"Madam! Your luggage!" he repeated more insistently, and he eagerly reached for her bags. There were two men, she now realized, and they were quite possibly stealing her things.

She protested, "No, I—"

"*Anyu!*" Tonye cried out, the Hungarian word for mother. He tugged on her skirt, jostling Ebinimi, who began to wail.

"I don't—please," she repeated, scooping up Ebinimi, but the men had already placed her bags on a cart, and, out of the corner of her eye, she saw Obi wandering toward the luggage return. She would have to trust the men. With a few quick steps forward, she caught the child by the back of his shirt, tugging him back to the group, and the four of them followed the men—and their luggage—through the airport.

Her underarms were damp and her hair was plastered onto the back of her neck. The children were sweaty as well, still in the sweaters and coats they'd donned in Manchester. But for the moment, all she could do was walk.

"Madam," the taller of the two men asked, "where are you going?"

She realized then that she had no idea. Having followed the men through customs, somehow getting the children through the hurdles of the international transfer, she now felt a tightening in her chest. She was lost.

Suddenly, like a ray of hope, she saw his face.

"Jutka!" her husband called. He seemed to relish this form of her name, sometimes wandering around the house murmuring it over and over, "Jutka, Jutka, Jutka."

The sound was like music.

"Mamah!"

The boys had seen him first. Barreling toward their father, they threatened to overtake him, and she laughed, the joy of the moment relieving a bit of her fear.

"Welcome to Nigeria," he said, Obi and Tonye clinging to him. She reached over the boys to kiss him.

She was so proud of him, graduating—with a Ph.D.!—and landing the job at Shell.

As the family crossed the threshold into their new country, she took in the strange, unfamiliar landscape and a feeling of uncertainty buzzed around her like a cloud of gnats. Everywhere they went, things seemed to hum, the sound of traffic and voices ubiquitous.

For the first time, she feared she was ill-equipped for the challenge of raising the children here. She wasn't even sure she could keep herself safe.

Tamping down her nerves, she followed Matthew to the car. Shell had provided a chauffeur who, to her utter amazement, managed to fit all of their luggage into the car with them—several piled in the front passenger seat while everyone crammed in the back.

But as the car pulled away from the airport, she felt even more intimidated. There were street lights and "flyovers," a strange phenomenon where bridges crossed over land, elevating one line of speeding cars over another. Sometimes people stood by the side of the road, waving at cars. She asked Matthew why, and he grinned.

"They're trying to get a taxi," he chuckled. "They wave at every car in case one is willing to take them."

She just shrugged. If there was such demand for taxis, why didn't they have taxi stations? Why are the taxis indistinguishable from other cars?

And then there was the issue of electricity.

When they arrived at the Shell guest house in Lagos, she was glad to find that the accommodation was well-equipped, complete with a generator. However, when they arrived at their new home in Port Harcourt the next day, the power was out. A cold dread pulsed through her veins as Matthew flipped the living room light switch up and down, without success.

He let out a frustrated huff, "NEPA!"

NEPA.

Technically the acronym for Nigeria's power authority, it soon became a mantra of indignation. The outages often lasted for several hours, and they were an inconvenience Judit wasn't accustomed to.

Still, the house was nice enough. Situated in the Rumubiakani district of Port Harcourt, the modest two-bedroom home had been painted blue inside and out, the pale color shiny against the unfinished gray stone floor. Matthew had purchased a dining table with six chairs—a nice touch, since it would allow them to share meals together—but the rest of the house was empty.

She vowed to make the best of things.

After all, Manchester hadn't been without struggle, either, and she'd managed to survive. While she hoped things would be easier here, she knew she could handle anything that came her way.

Mercifully, many things seemed to improve the longer they were in Nigeria. The neighbors, in particular, seemed very friendly. Fascinated by her pale skin—she was the only white person in the subdivision—they called her "*oyibo*," a local term used to describe white or light-skinned foreigners. Her mixed-race children, she learned, were also considered oyibo, and yet, neighbors were quick to accept them, even coming to the house to welcome the family on their first day in town.

It brought fascinating cultural traditions right to her door. With their elaborate hairstyles and brightly-colored clothing, Nigerian women captivated her. Some had their hair threaded or, as they called it, plaited—pronounced to rhyme with matted—in which varying lengths of hair were tightly wound across their lengths using black thread. It supposedly helped the hair grow longer and healthier.

With hair unsuitable for such styles, Judit settled for wearing headscarves, both a way to add some color to her outfit and a practical item in the heat of the day. She easily adapted to Nigerian clothing, finding the wrappers worn around the waist practical and comfortable. She wasn't bothered much by the little things— the oranges, for example, weren't orange at all, but green. In those cases, she shrugged and laughed, reminding herself of the fascinating new perspective she was gaining on the world.

But, while she found her new home intriguing in many ways, she missed her home more than ever before, particularly as Christmas, her favorite holiday, approached. Nigerians, like the British, didn't celebrate the coming of Little Jesus on Christmas Eve.

Still, she persisted in the traditions of her childhood, asking Matthew to take the children for the night on Christmas Eve so she could set up the skinny white tree—adorning it with a single garland and a few ornaments—and lay out the presents.

They sang, too, in the language of her home. *"Mennyből az angyal,"* they warbled, welcoming the angel from heaven to earth. *"Lejött hozzátok."*

They shared hugs and kisses and a spread of chicken, rice, and yam as well as jam-filled cream pastries. For Matthew, she'd prepared a separate plate of chopped red hot peppers to satisfy his craving for exceptionally spicy food.

But she was totally unprepared for what she saw the next day. As she walked into the living room, she heard something strange outside. She opened the door and gasped.

Several people were dancing and entertaining as they paraded through the neighborhood. A growing crowd followed the performance as they slowed in front of each house. These were not the typical Bethlehemers she was used to in Hungary. There was a drummer and a masked dancer in a demonic yet feminine costume. The mask was carved out of light-colored wood. There were three performers altogether: a drummer, a dancer, and one who solicited money. The last came up to the terrace, expecting to be paid for their service.

Unsure of what to do, Judit stepped back into the house and watched the passing event through the window panes.

It was a strange feeling to look out your own window and realize that the world outside was not your home. Having lived in Manchester, she knew the feeling would fade. She was bound to grow more accustomed to Nigeria.

But transitions could be brutal.

So she was even more grateful for the warm welcome she saw everywhere she went.

When they'd lived in Manchester, her father-in-law had written to her, welcoming her to the family and opening a line of communication between her and the Nigerian family. It meant a lot to her to be welcomed not only by the neighbors but by the family she'd gained by marrying Matthew.

She found *Opupapa* to be just as delightful in person—a wise, kind man, even if he did speak so quietly one often had to lean in to hear him.

Having never met him in person, she wasn't sure what to expect. Matthew had told her that his father bore the scars of smallpox—he'd told her the beautiful story of faith and love that had brought his parents together—but she wasn't sure what he would look like in person.

In truth, his facial scarring made him look somehow wiser and more regal, this man of God who had shown her such a warm welcome.

He was so very kind, even from the moment she opened the door to find him on the stoop, dressed in a traditional, blue two-piece Nigerian suit.

He embraced her right away, greeting her as his own daughter, and she thought she might collapse into him, grateful for the support of an elder.

She realized then how much she missed her own father, and Uncle Béla, too, and how much the maternal presence of her mother and Bori had propped her up all those years.

That sense of warmth and gratitude only increased as Opupapa sat with the boys. Still dressed in their school uniforms—crisp, white, embroidered shirts with blue shorts—they gravitated to him immediately, curious about their grandfather. Ebinimi joined in, of course, in the pink one-piece swimsuit she preferred in the heat of the day, gazing up at her Opupapa with wide, curious eyes.

Then Judit didn't feel so alone.

There was, after all, no reason to feel disappointed or sad about her life in Nigeria. While of course, she missed her home, this new world was full of excitement and intrigue. She could walk in nature and enjoy the unusual plants in her yard—the hibiscus flowers were her favorite, their beautiful, exotic, pink blooms unlike anything she'd seen in Hungary. Her children delighted in watching bananas grow from tiny stumps to sweet, pulpy fruit.

She knew the family enjoyed many nice things—certainly more than some of their neighbors. They even had two cars, an unimaginable luxury for so many.

They'd first purchased a white Volkswagen Beetle, and only a year later, they'd taken a second, a beautiful blue metallic Datsun Bluebird that allowed her to haul the children around town.

She struggled with driving in Nigeria at first. The laws seemed lax and unpredictable, and the roads were sometimes marred with enormous potholes and chaos. The city had only one traffic light—the district colloquially referred to as "Traffic Light"—less common than traffic policemen. Over time, as she adjusted to living in Nigeria, her driving followed suit and her confidence grew.

She could do this. She could build a new life here with her husband and beautiful children.

In a way, it felt good to drive. She prided herself on caring for the children, so if they needed to be taken somewhere—to school, the doctor, or something more fun—she could handle it. There was no need to call Matthew for such things. The children, too, became more independent as they grew, more easily carted along as she ran her day-to-day errands.

So she loaded the children into the car, and they made their way to the market, the three of them happy and giggling in the backseat. She let her mind wander a bit, then, considering how much she'd grown to love this place, even in the short time she'd been here. With a hint of disbelief, she thought of what an outsider she'd been when they first arrived. They hadn't lived in Nigeria long, but already she'd found a taste for the food—though she still missed some Hungarian foods—and an appreciation for the clothing and traditions.

The children had adapted, too. The sound of them chattering and singing rang out from the backseat.

And then everything changed.

The young girl came from nowhere.

She slammed on the car's brakes. A horrible thump echoed against the front bumper. Her eyes met the girl's for a brief moment, each reflecting the other's horror.

Without thinking, she threw the car into park and flung the door open, crying out to the young teenager who now lay on the ground, clenching her teeth as she writhed slowly from side to side in pain. It looked like her thigh was swollen.

And suddenly, Judit was an outsider again.

A crowd gathered, staring down at the two of them as Judit crouched with the girl, uncertain of what to do. She feared for what might happen to the girl, and how the crowd might react to her. Her heart sank when she recalled that there was no emergency line, no ambulance, no immediate medical assistance.

So she scooped the girl up as best she could, placing her in the front seat of the car with the help of some nearby onlookers. Unsure of where exactly to go, she sped over to the Shell camp clinic.

And as she did, she prayed for them both.

Chapter 15

OPUMAMA

MATTHEW HATED TO SEE HIS wife like this. Wracked with guilt, her hands shook as she told him the story of the girl, no more than a teenager, who had stepped out in front of her car.

He listened, concern like a knot in his gut. At least, he reassured her, the girl hadn't died. He knew of at least two Shell employees who had lost their lives in road accidents over the past few years, and, while Nigerian roads had never been particularly safe, the accident rate had been rising recently—over thirty percent of the company's vehicles had been involved in accidents the previous year.

Her accident could have been worse. Much worse.

Imagining his entire family in that car, he shuddered to think what might have happened.

"I didn't know what to do." Judit lamented in Hungarian, her voice shaky. "I thought they were going to beat me or the children," referring to the crowd of onlookers that formed around the scene.

"Don't think about that." He drew her into what he hoped was a soothing embrace, her shoulder blades like rocks beneath his hands. "I will find out what I can do. It will be fine."

Months earlier, they'd taken in a young 'house girl', who would complete chores in their home for money, room, and board. It was a common practice in the city, he'd explained. Still, she'd insisted on traveling to meet the girl's family. "If she were my child," she'd said, "I would want to know who was looking after her."

He knew she'd feel the same about the poor girl she'd hit with the car. After she'd rushed the girl in the front seat to the Shell Clinic, clinic personnel there had gotten in touch with the girl's family and stated they would not treat her, as she was not an employee or family member of someone in the company.

Matthew offered to pay for the x-ray and whatever treatment would be necessary elsewhere. While the family was grateful for his offer, they chose instead to take the girl to a native healer whom her relatives trusted.

He'd seen that kind of distrust his entire life—public services in Nigeria weren't always stable, and, in the people's eyes, not always trustworthy. In a way, he understood it. He'd always prided him-self on his logic and level-headedness. Now that he had children of his own, he sometimes felt a pang of apprehension—he'd wanted to know they would be safe. He waved those thoughts away as best he could. After all, children had been children since the beginning of time, and their antics rarely caused any actual harm.

Still, he hated to take them places where he couldn't control the situation—where things seemed unfamiliar, unstable, or po-tentially dangerous.

That included his home village.

Ever since they'd arrived in Nigeria, Judit had been trying to convince him to take the children to his hometown.

"Why is this important?" he'd asked her, although he already knew the answer. Even though his parents had both visited them in Port Harcourt, she wanted the children to see where he'd grown up. She wanted to see it herself, too.

Against his better judgement, he arranged a visit to Otuogidi, Ogbia, where his mother lived. It would be short, he emphasized to both Judit and the children. They couldn't risk getting stuck in a village with no plumbing or electricity and nowhere for them to stay.

It felt overly risky to him. But when he finally gave in, Judit looked so happy.

So one Saturday afternoon, he led the family to the water park where they approached a man with a commercial speedboat. With a single glance at Matthew's family—he could practically read the word "oyibo" flashing across the man's mind—the boat driver quoted them a rate that was well above market value.

"Mpschww," Matthew sighed dismissively, "Dis man, you are not serious. Make I find betta pesin," he continued in pidgin as he feigned walking towards one of the driver's competitors.

Eventually, the family climbed aboard the man's speedboat for the two-hour trip to Ogbia.

It had been years since he first traveled to Port Harcourt. So many things had seemed unusual to him back then, from the brick buildings to the shoes to the shiny vehicles on paved roads.

Now those modern amenities seemed comforting and familiar—and Ogbia seemed strange. The land still felt like his home, but traveling with his wife and children was like transporting them back in time to a place they didn't fit—a place they shouldn't fit.

He steadied himself by watching his family's curious faces. Always fascinated by rural Nigeria's flora and fauna, his wife's face was a mix of apprehension and pure joy. She gripped the side of the boat as though her life depended on it. When they passed a row of mangrove trees, their roots protruding out into the water, Judit gasped, her eyes wide and bright.

"*Elképesztő*!" she exclaimed, truly amazed by the tangled bramble of the trees' bases. "It looks like they were drug out by giants."

He smiled then, although he would not allow himself to fully relax until this hectic trip was over and the children were home safe in their beds.

Despite his apprehension, he enjoyed watching Judit marvel over his home country. She frequently crouched down to observe the fish that occasionally breached the surface or a small crab that hobbled along the sand. When he watched her gaze up at the towering palm trees—a plant he took for granted—it was like seeing his home through fresh eyes.

Soon they reached the nearest river bank. When the speedboat driver held out his hand, Matthew helped his family clamber out of the boat, careful to keep the children from getting too muddy or wet.

As they made their way toward his mother's house, they would soon acquire a growing entourage of random villagers, mostly children, excited and curious about the new visitors.

A naked little boy darted toward the river and leaped in. Several other children were bobbing in and out of the river, and the boy's head soon emerged, spitting water at them through the gap in his front teeth. Floating by, buoyed on the dark, murky water, was a grimy plastic bottle.

Had the water been so dirty when he was a child?

He shook off the thought. It didn't matter, really. He'd been accustomed to the Riverine life back then, but his children only swam in the crystal-clear Shell Club pool. Since their move to Port Harcourt, they'd spent many happy days lounging around the luxurious space, enjoying the soft drinks and food served to them by the club's waiters.

Sometimes he wondered if they would ever grow tired of splashing around in the pool. As if on a constant loop, the children would leap into the pool, climb out, shuffle around the edge, then jump in again, squealing as they did. Judit would sit on the sidelines reminding them, "don't run!" and "slow down!"

They needed to be reminded. Like all kids, they forgot that the world could be a hard place, even in the sparkling, chemically treated water of the Shell Club pool—to say nothing of the village where he'd grown up.

It had been safe for him, back then at least, and it was probably safe for Ogbian children today. They'd grown up here, after all, and were attuned to the particular dangers of village life. But his children had never experienced the life of his childhood.

"Oh, oh, oh, oh, oh!"

His mother's characteristic excitement jostled him from his distraction as the older woman threw her arms around his wife. His mother was thin, almost frail, with dark skin and a patch of dark hair peeking out from beneath her deep purple head wrap. Her greeting was a type of universal language, the sound of glee and excitement translating through her high-pitched tone, but he knew his wife would understand little else his mother said. Having never learned English, his mother tended to ramble primarily in Ogbian.

"Mama, *alua*!" Matthew greeted.

She approached him and took his hand, smiling up at him, before leading the family back into the little red-brown mud house.

Judit had met his mother once before. His younger sister, Dorcas, had traveled with her and Matthew's young niece to Port Harcourt, and she'd greeted Judit similarly then, heaping praise and gratitude onto her at a level he thought might overwhelm her. When his sister had handed her a beautiful Nigerian dress, Judit later confessed, she'd worried that she would seem inadequate as a host and wife.

There was no need to worry about that. His mother had clearly liked her from the time she first laid eyes on her, even urging the two to have more children.

They'd exchanged a knowing glance then—neither of them was interested in having more children. Still, Judit had beamed at his mother's suggestion, and he was glad she saw it as a sign of acceptance and love.

He knew she was excited to see his mother again. They couldn't stay long. Eager to get home—or, more accurately, fearful that they wouldn't be able to find a speedboat if they stayed too long—Matthew only afforded the visit an hour or so.

As he watched the children with his mother, he wondered about her health. He'd heard about her physical ailments—although she seemed mostly healthy, from time to time his sister had written to him asking for money or medicine.

But there was always more that lingered beneath the surface.

Gradually, she'd grown paranoid some time back, though it was not clear when it had started. When people passed by her on the street, she would scrunch her face and suck her teeth, causing many of the villagers to question what they had done to upset her. More troubling, she'd concluded that his father had been unfaithful. This made it impossible for the marriage to continue in any traditional way. Although he couldn't know whether her

contention was true, he did know that his father was deeply saddened by their separation.

Her warmth, though, hadn't changed since he was a child.
Doting on her grandchildren, she remarked in Ogbian at how
large they'd grown.

She was right. Now nearly seven years old, the boys had become
quite independent, outgrowing their Army Children's School blue
and white uniforms at a troubling pace. Ebinimi, too, was much
bigger now, her little personality clearer and bolder than when
she'd last seen her *opumama*.

He wondered how big his children would be when they next
saw her. Despite his sense that it would be some time before their
next visit, he still didn't want to stay long. The family said their
goodbyes, Matthew leaving some money with his mother—she
graciously accepted it, with a word of how proud she was of
Matthew and his family.

Before they returned home, he'd promised one more stop.
They trekked through the imposing forest, with dense trees on
both sides, en route to Oloibiri. The first site in the country to
discover oil, the little village remained difficult to access, despite
its historic importance. With no roads connecting the village to
his mother's and no speedboats in sight, Matthew flagged down a
canoe, paddled by a boy who looked to be no older than fourteen
or fifteen.

He saw Judit's breath catch in her throat then.

Sometimes, he underestimated how unsettling these everyday
occurrences were for someone who hadn't grown up with them.
The canoe rocked side to side, and Matthew saw his wife's grip
tighten, one hand on the side of the vessel and the other around
Ebinimi's shoulders. He, too, would have preferred to travel any

other way, but to move between Ogbia's lesser populated communities was to do as the Ogbians did.

So they hunkered down in the canoe, overlooking the way the water splashed high on its sides, sometimes trickling over into it.

When they reached Oloibiri, a priest walked them to the parsonage where Matthew lived as a child while his father was posted there. These towns were sadly in a very poor state, even though much of the country's oil came from here. Rivers State, unlike most others, was overlooked every time the federal government created new states. This meant fewer federal nairas were allocated to develop the poor and desolate areas.

Having lived in several different places since his youth in Ogbia, Matthew hated to see the desolation now more than ever. There simply was no reason for the government's disregard for this region and its people.

This, more than anything before, jarred him. When he looked back on his childhood—when he saw the children splashing in the waters where he'd learned to swim—he wondered how many times the Ogbian people had hoped for change. Or, more accurately, he wondered how often he had hoped for change.

He recalled his optimism when Rivers State was formed, the way the country reeled at news of the coup d'état, and the renewed hope that had settled over Nigeria when the war ended. How quickly—how stealthily—the years had passed since then, and yet, precious little had changed in his home village.

Meanwhile, his children had learned to swim, Shell's swimming trainer holding their little bellies as they kicked and paddled, grinning when their faces emerged, dripping and sputtering.

He was teaching them to play chess, too, a game of strategy that conditioned its players to think several moves ahead. When they were six, he enrolled the boys in their first chess tournament to foster a competitive drive.

With a pang of nostalgia and pride, he considered how remarkably different their childhoods would be from his own—how many more places they had seen in their young lives than he had in his first two decades.

Perhaps this was the secret, hidden reward of aiming high and shooting high—to raise your children with so much more than you'd ever dreamed of as a child.

And, although he'd already exceeded his parents' wildest dreams, he had bigger plans.

He'd worked at Shell for years by then, and as often as was prudent, he pushed the higher-ups to allow his family to move to Shell Camp. Like the Shell Club where they lounged by the pool year-round, Shell Camp was decidedly upscale—the employee housing there had reliable electricity and running water, plus the many perks of a wealthier community.

No matter how hard he pushed, the company consistently rejected him, stating that they simply didn't have the room in such a high-demand area. Shell Camp seemed to remain populated with a disproportionate number of British expatriates.

It felt unfair. Although he was a junior employee, he had a great deal of training and experience—he even had a Ph.D. He was a dedicated and loyal worker. However, having only worked a few years at the company, Matthew remained at a disadvantage to those who had nearly a decade under their belt. Still, he firmly believed he had proven himself valuable.

With every new request, the denials got firmer and more final.

But finally offered him a compromise.

The house at Ranami Abah wasn't in Shell Camp, but it was, at least, in an exclusive gated community. A sizable house, it had four bedrooms plus a generator that could provide backup electricity when NEPA failed them.

Despite the upgrade, he was soon offered a job at Shell Lagos.

The new position offered new opportunities, surely the next step in his drive to succeed. Determined to make major changes to the company—and resolved that a leadership position was the best way to reach his goal—he hoped the new position would finally grant him the power to support Nigerian workers.

He'd noticed unfairness at Shell for years. The housing denials impacted him and his family, but discrimination extended across the board. British workers often received higher-level positions for which they earned more money than most Nigerian workers at the same levels. As a man born and bred in the region, he knew well both the wealth of resources and how those resources had supported the people of his country.

He wanted more for them.

Most importantly, he wanted more for his children.

Even if he couldn't bring more equity to his company—a point that he wasn't at all prepared to accept as final—he could push his children, just as his father had pushed him.

Chapter 16

DOUBLE DOUBLE

~~~~~~~

BEING MARRIED TO SUCH AN ambitious man could be challenging. Matthew's accomplishments were impressive, to say nothing of his persistence. Most of all, Judit marveled at Matthew's sense of purpose.

She'd hoped, as a teenager, that lightning would strike, giving her clear direction for her life's choices. Back then she'd hoped that, if she prayed enough, she would suddenly realize the true meaning of her life—that God would send her a sign. That sign never came.

Worried that she was floating through life—missing out on some great calling—she'd done what she could to finish her education and find a good job.

Aside from marrying Matthew, she hadn't felt all that certain about anything.

Except for her children.

As she comforted the squalling Ebinimi—the poor thing had pinched her finger in the door—she felt silly for ever having questioned her life's meaning.

She had three beautiful, smart, motivated, kind, warm children. What more purpose could she want?

In truth, there was little she could reasonably ask for at all. Matthew's new job with the West African Glass Industry—WAGI, they called it—had propelled the family into modern comforts they hadn't dreamed of just a few years earlier.

The job also carried the possibility of travel to the company's partnering European factories. She hoped deeply for that. While she'd adjusted to their Nigerian home, she missed Hungary deeply. That was the life of the immigrant, she assumed. As heavy as the thought made her heart feel, there was no point in dwelling on it. She would be okay, as she'd always been.

What mattered was that Matthew was gaining some real sway in his workplace. A very desirable position, the leadership role he held carried a lot of responsibility.

They had been invited to move into a house in the former Government Residential Area in Port Harcourt. Although the new home within the gated neighborhood, O.C.C. Estate, was a little smaller than the previous, it was big enough for their family. Judit could easily imagine them growing used to it, once the necessary repairs were completed. The boys immediately took to the little guava tree outside, laughing and climbing its trunk.

Matthew had often come home from work with a type of buzz about him. Brimming with excitement over the possibilities, he'd rattled off the words of encouragement he'd received that day, promises for higher pay and more influence. His boss liked him, that much was clear, and Matthew seemed so certain that things would work out—that he would move up the ladder swiftly. With a contagious enthusiasm, he zipped around the house, dreaming of the things they'd fix up, the new opportunities the children would have once his promotion came through.

But Judit knew well enough that the promise of promotion carried with it a level of stress that sometimes bled through to his home life—but perhaps that was simply her own anxiety, projected onto him.

Ebinimi's wailing started to subside, and Judit looked at the girl's little finger. "Shhh," she whispered, although even as she quieted the girl, she felt her own stomach turn. With the deep purplish red spreading down the digit, she wondered whether the little one might lose her fingernail.

She felt the pain along with her daughter.

As the three children grew older, she'd hoped parenting would be easier. Instead, late-night diaper changes and feedings were replaced with other worries.

Since the boys' second-grade year had concluded, she'd found herself increasingly concerned about them. Both boys were smart and kind. Obi excelled in music, and, when she could get him to sit and listen, he had a promising sense of melody and rhythm. He'd taken to swimming quickly, although he preferred dog paddling over actual strokes. With his hyperactive personality, he could be difficult to handle at times. On the other hand, Tonye was shy and quiet, perhaps an asset to his success at school—he was perfectly content to listen patiently.

Maybe that was the difference. Just their personalities.

Whatever the cause, when their second-grade report cards had come in, Tonye had passed. Obi had failed.

She'd felt a stab of guilt then, realizing how difficult the result would be on Obi. From the time they were born—even before, actually—they'd done everything together. Her heart broke to think of Tonye advancing while Obi didn't.

But, as Matthew pointed out, neither would it be fair to make Tonye repeat second grade with his brother.

And the sorrow she felt for both was eclipsed by that familiar motherly guilt.

Before they'd moved to Nigeria, she'd wanted them to experience a European elementary school. They were a bit young, that was true, but they were smart and capable. She'd convinced the school in Hungary to place the five-year-olds in the first-grade class.

They'd seemed to be doing quite well. So, when they got to Nigeria, they were enrolled in the second grade halfway through the academic year.

Perhaps it had been a mistake. They were only five years old and completing their second grade. Even if they repeated the year, they'd still be younger than most of their peers.

But how could she expect Tonye to repeat a grade he'd passed?

If his twin advanced, what would staying behind do to Obi?

The move, along with their father's new job, made the conundrum even more difficult.

In the end, they'd decided to re-enroll Obi in second grade, putting him with some other children his age. Tonye could go on to third. Of course, she'd wanted them to move through school together—and perhaps they would, eventually—but for now, this seemed best for both.

In a way, they still got to learn together. She loved helping them explore new topics, a natural extension of her previous dreams of teaching. With all the energy she could muster, she tried to bring concepts to life for them, pushing them to develop their own interests and skills.

She still sometimes wondered what her own goals should be—particularly in a home that placed such an emphasis on achievement—she found that she had little energy for anything other than her children.

She didn't need anything else.

Once upon a time, she'd dreamed of having five children. She almost chuckled to think of it now. Back then, she'd reasoned that, since she was the fifth child, she should have five little ones, too. She'd been fond of critiquing family planning, arguing that, if her parents had limited the number of children in the family, she wouldn't have been born at all!

That version of herself seemed impossibly young.

Anyway, God had a way of doing what was best, even if she didn't realize it. The years flew by—her babies growing into children—and she focused on taking in the wonders of their childhoods. She would never have these moments again, when her little ones were discovering what they loved and hated, their quirky personalities, expressing themselves in ways that sometimes made her laugh and at other times overwhelmed her with nostalgia.

She'd once come in to find the boys wearing Matthew's traditional Nigerian attire.

With his father's hat perched low against his ears, Tonye had declared, "We're just like Apu!"

She'd laughed until a tear escaped the corner of her eye, her two silly little boys joining in the laughter even as they affected their father's proud stance.

They were each so different—unique and special in their own way. Tonye with his picky diet—sometimes going for days with only bread and tea, refusing anything else offered. Obi with his big, funny personality, prone to coming to his brother's defense. And Ebinimi, her little girl who didn't act little at all. From her first words, she'd seemed impossibly mature, her fierce sense of fairness and stubborn attitude had her holding to her opinion, no matter what.

With each new development, she felt a pang of pride and an ache of sorrow. Each new growth period signaled their eventual adulthood as they tugged slightly away from her, testing their independence before scurrying back to cling to her skirt.

At thirty-nine years old, she'd more than resolved herself to raising just three children. Her hair was longer, and she wore her large round glasses all the time now. Her periods had become irregular, some no more than spotting, others skipped altogether. While it was a bit earlier than most, she could feel herself moving into menopause.

She planned to mention the changes to her doctor during her regular checkup in December.

Instead, he'd come into the room with a huge grin. "You're pregnant!" he'd declared. The abdominal x-ray brought even more shocking news.

She wasn't just pregnant.

She was estimated to be six-months pregnant. And it was twins again.

Maybe a small part of her had known. She'd thought it strange how similar some of the symptoms of menopause were to her previous pregnancies. It certainly explained the missed periods.

She'd been certain she was too old for children.

And yet, the family once again prepared to welcome two new babies, the anticipation growing with her abdomen.

She thought a lot about her age, then. Not only had she believed she was beyond childbearing years, but she also wondered at the way the round numbers seemed to signal something else—perhaps something spiritual.

She'd been thirty when the boys were born. Already older than most of her peers, she'd been so relieved when the babies were healthy. And now, exactly ten years later at forty, two more little ones were coming.

Surely it couldn't be a coincidence to have twins twice, at round decade ages. Doubtful, she thought. Perhaps God meant it as a sign. She'd trusted him when she thought she was done having children—and maybe he meant to show her that she should keep trusting.

Still, living in Nigeria now, it was difficult to trust that everything would be okay. She had much less support here than she'd had back in Europe, for one thing. And she would need some help caring for two twin babies on top of the three children.

Perhaps sensing her concern, her sister Aci had agreed to come after the twins were born with any necessary supplements. The children were more excited about the Hungarian toys they hoped she'd bring. And, of course, they loved their "Aci *néni*."

Judit mostly looked forward to her sister's company. In this new world, where she had few friends and limited adult communication, the loneliness sometimes hung like a fog. Pregnancy only compounded things. In her earlier pregnancies, she'd had family around all the time—they'd doted on her, brought gifts, asked how she was doing.

But, more than that, they'd dreamed with her. They had wondered with her about whether the babies would look like her or Matthew, whether they would be premature or big and hearty, when they would arrive, how big she would grow, and how excited they were to meet them.

She had Matthew for those things, of course. And the three little ones at home asked a lot of questions.

But it wasn't the same.

As grateful as she was for Aci to come and help, she knew her sister wouldn't stay forever. Eventually, she'd have to return home.

How would she raise twins at her age? While she still felt relatively young, she'd struggled with the boys, and that was ten years earlier. While she hoped they were aging into an easier stage of child-rearing, their pre-teen years carried their own challenges.

During his fifth year of primary school, Tonye passed the secondary school entrance exam and advanced early, skipping the final year of primary school. He would become the youngest student at Stella Maris College. Where most began the six years of secondary school at age eleven or twelve, he started at nine years old.

Two years ahead of his brother.

The tension in the house built, and Judit worried a lot about the effect of Tonye's success on his twin. Although they allowed him to complete his first year at Stella Maris, Matthew had pulled Tonye aside and encouraged him to take the entrance exam to higher-ranked schools. Tonye repeating the first year, they contended, would be good for both boys.

She didn't have long to think about it. With only a few months' notice, two new Mamahs were on their way. When she felt that first pinch, gentler than full labor but impossible to ignore nonetheless, she knew right away.

Excited and anxious, she and Matthew made their way to the Halten Clinic—the small clinic looked less like a hospital and more like a large house—as the clock crept toward midnight. The nurse checked them in, and a midwife stood by, too. Ready or not, the babies were coming.

But they were coming on their own time, it turned out.

When the nurse checked her cervix, she sighed, remarking, "Nothing will be happening until eight in the morning."

"Will she be okay 'til tomorrow?" Matthew asked.

"She will be fine. We will take care of her, sah!"

Judit smiled and nodded. "I'll be fine," she reassured him, sending him home to be with the other children.

She didn't need him there, after all. She'd done this twice before.

But as soon as he was gone, her heart quickened in her chest.

She'd become more comfortable in her new adopted city, but she still struggled to communicate. When the searing pain of labor came in the hours to come, would she be able to find the English words she needed? She thought, then, of calling Matthew back.

The nurse and midwife didn't seem concerned, and there was no reason to believe he wouldn't be back long before those crucial hours arrived.

So she tried to sleep while there was still a chance for it, the contractions making sleep more and more impossible as the night wore on.

When the nurse checked her just a few hours later, her eyes grew wide.

"Please go and call him," she exclaimed, her voice tinny and sharp, and the midwife, who'd been standing by, ran out the door.

Judit forgot her practiced breathing for a moment, and an unexpected contraction threatened to fold her in half. It would take time for someone to reach the doctor, requiring a bicycle ride to his home. At this rate, he would never make it back in time.

Breathe, she reminded herself. Breathe. If she could stay calm, maybe she could convince these babies to hold on.

Minute after minute passed, and the doctor didn't appear.

Another squeeze pinched her lower abdomen, and she fought against the waves of pain and nausea. Forty-five minutes, then fifty minutes, then an hour passed. Still, there was no sign of the doctor.

Another wave of screaming, pinching pain wracked her body.

"*Itt van*?!" she cried, forgetting herself for a moment. "Is he here?!"

"Breathe," the nurse said. "Remember to—"

The lights suddenly died, the equipment going silent.

"NEPA!" someone yelled in the hallway.

Then pure panic ensued.

The shock distracted her from the pain, at least.

"Start the generator!" someone called.

But the generator didn't start, an effect, she gathered, of the night guard having gone to get the doctor.

The small hospital had fallen into pandemonium, but she couldn't focus on that. As the screaming fire in her abdomen grew more intense, so did the insatiable urge to push.

"Breathe," the nurse repeated.

Judit could have screamed at her. Instead, she focused, letting out a cry from deep in her chest.

When the midwife lit the lantern, holding it so the nurse could check her progress, Judit knew what she would say.

They couldn't wait.

Finally, mercifully, she pushed.

Her twin girls were tiny and came so easy compared to her other children, all of whom had been quite large. Thinner in their limbs than the chubby-cheeked babies she had previously delivered, they each took in their first breaths of their new world. They were quite somnolent and, like all of her children, they were beautiful and perfect.

The only light was the glow of the midwife's lantern. But it was enough to see her beautiful girls.

"What are their names?" asked the nurse.

"Marika and Te—" she began, before correcting herself. "In English, Maria and Theresa!"

Two names with such significance to Judit's Catholic faith, being shared with the mother of Jesus and the 'living Saint' Mother Teresa.

The world would know her daughters by their English names, but she would always call them by their diminutive, Marika and Terike. Her little tribute to Hungary, the names were often paired in her culture, like Jack and Jill or Peter and Paul in anglophone countries. At the moment though, there was no time to savor her experience with her two little ones.

Judit was directed to a detached washroom. She was fatigued yet strong enough to walk. She walked slowly, slightly wide-legged. She was relieved it was dark outside and no one could see her as she walked across the yard. Though this much movement so soon after birth felt foreign and strange to her, she took comfort in knowing that she would soon return to her baby girls.

That night, she cradled Marika in her arms as they slept. The baby seemed too cold, nearly shivering, Judit thought. Without an incubator—which would otherwise be impossible to use without the generator running—then she would have to incubate the old-fashioned way.

NEPA could do as they pleased. With or without them, the Mamah girls would get through the night. She knew, then, that they would be okay.

Chapter 17

CHIEF

～～～

MOST OF MATTHEW'S COWORKERS disliked Mr. Hariprasad. A middle-aged Indian man who had somehow earned Nigerian citizenship, his personality was abrasive at best. And yet, Matthew had forged a friendship with him. He might even describe them as close.

When the twins had been born in March, Hariprasad had congratulated him, a conversation that one of Matthew's fellow employees had marveled at.

"Ah, you like dis man? *Na wa o!*" Rob had remarked, a tinge of jealousy turning his voice cold.

Matthew had just shrugged. In truth, he didn't care much whether his coworkers liked their boss. Being one of the few workers Hariprasad liked could be a good thing—after all, his manager was set to retire soon and Matthew knew of no more qualified successor than himself.

As time wore on, his plan began to materialize. WAGI first promoted him to Marketing Manager, before awarding him a new, higher-paying role as Financial Controller. While the long hours weren't ideal—especially with two infants and three other children at home—he pressed on, cheerfully agreeing when he was asked to escort potential clients to dinner or other events.

He'd worked long hours to complete his doctorate. Despite Judit's concerns, he would do so again.

Things weren't so bad, he reminded her. Since his teenage years, the country's political culture had been in turmoil. He'd seen his plans dashed—or at least he'd thought he had—by coups and uprisings for as long as he remembered.

This job, on the other hand, was stable.

Among the most accomplished and highly-educated of the company's workers, he had longevity at WAGI. He truly appreciated, for once, holding a position that wasn't completely upset by political unrest.

Around the time he and Judit had learned they were expecting their second set of twins, another wave of political jockeying had upset Nigeria's governmental structure. Several military officers had conspired against the country's first democratically elected president, Shehu Shagari. The state of optimism surrounding the election had been refreshing. But then the coup had installed yet another military head of state in Major General Muhammadu Buhari.

The country was once more plunged into a state of uncertainty.

In a way, it didn't surprise him—at least not as it had the first time his country had turned upside down. He remembered those times, the years of siege, of death, starvation, and lack of medicine, when he'd been forced to flee his school. He remembered seeing Port Harcourt—his first home after the village—lose its sheen under the pressure of war.

After those experiences, not much rattled him, but his life had changed a lot since that first coup. As a teenager, he'd been responsible for himself and himself alone. Now, his wife and children needed his affection and encouragement, and, even more than that, they needed financial stability.

That was why he was so grateful to have a good, stable job with good, stable people he enjoyed working alongside.

Politics could change your plans in an instant. Unless you were directly involved—and even then—there wasn't much you could do to protect yourself.

His tiny infant daughters grew bigger and stronger in those months of military rule, and Matthew pressed on, steadying himself in his work and waiting for the coming retirement of his boss and friend, Hariprasad.

Until the announcement.

WAGI's board of directors had appointed a new leader for the company. Except they hadn't hired a new General Manager. They'd hired a Managing Director. As a rule, General Managers at state-owned companies had to be Nigerian citizens.

But there was no such rule for Managing Directors.

So in a hard swerve, WAGI had renamed the position, creating a loophole that allowed them to hire a British expatriate: James P. Wayman.

Wayman exuded confidence despite his timid, shuffle-like walk with short strides. Slightly paunchy, he seemed to almost lean back as he moved around the offices. He had a signature laugh, like Matthew, except Wayman's laugh bore a hint of mockery. Almost a cackle, he would pinch his eyes shut as his jaw retreated into the ample folds of his neck. He looked ridiculous, at least to Matthew, and yet, a former Lieutenant Colonel of the British Army, he somehow gave the effect of looking down on everyone he spoke with, including the highest-ranking managers in the company.

He was Matthew's new supervisor.

While his former boss wasn't well-liked by his coworkers—the feeling was mutual for most—Hariprasad at least seemed fair and, if not quite kind, never cruel. Quiet and withdrawn, he emerged only to give feedback, which he did with a militant efficiency that often read as blunt. But Matthew understood him. For Hariprasad, correcting them wasn't about feeling superior, but about making sure the work was done well.

The approach resonated with Matthew, who identified with his former manager and friend's persistence.

It was the complete opposite of Wayman's style.

Perhaps, he reasoned, he hadn't given the new manager a chance. He had hoped for the job himself, after all. Maybe his distrust of Wayman came from the disappointment of being passed over for a role he'd long had his eye on.

He was disappointed. Judit reminded him there was no need to be. He'd received a promotion, too. As the new Assistant General Manager, he held the next highest rank at the company. A stepping stone to the role he wanted, he would simply need to make the most of the new job so that he was undeniably right for the promotion when Wayman's two-year tenure drew to a close.

There were perks to his new job. Their cream-colored house would be fully furnished, and he would have a company car—perhaps even one with a radio—as well as a driver, all marks of professional accomplishment that most Nigerians never reached.

All he could do was make the best of it.

It shouldn't be difficult, Matthew thought. Although Wayman initially gave him a squeamish feeling, he'd always gotten along with British people. There was the Shell employee who'd introduced him to ice as a young boy. Kind and easy-going, that man became something like a role model despite the brevity of their exchange. He'd spent time in Manchester, of course, working alongside British colleagues as he completed his doctoral studies.

And there was Miss Owen, the British missionary who arranged the gift of the motorized canoe for his father.

Matthew could never forget how much it eased his father's work and allowed him to transport Matthew to the safety of Warri so he could continue school during the war.

He loved that canoe.

Most Nigerians had some admiration for the British, but after the gift of the motorized canoe, Matthew had a fondness for the country that only increased during his schooling in the United Kingdom.

Better yet, Wayman had come to the company from Bendel State, a place Matthew was familiar with. Not only had he fled there to Warri during the war, but he'd also returned to the state when it came time to complete his NYSC service. Matthew was fascinated when he learned that Wayman had been bestowed the title of a traditional Nigerian chief in Ughelli—an unusual role for a foreigner.

He should have shared much in common with his new boss. So, despite rumors that Wayman had been sacked from the glass industry by Bendel State's governor, he tried to be open to a good working relationship with the middle-aged man.

He would need it, after all. As the company was now set up, department heads were to speak to Matthew about any concerns, ideas for improvement, equipment and supply orders, and other day-to-day issues. Matthew would then either advise the workers on the next steps or speak with the Managing Director to work out a solution.

Wayman wasn't far into his tenure when the first sign of trouble cropped up.

Matthew had stopped by to speak to the factory manager, Mr. Osaigbovo—another Bendelite—just to check in. An entire week without a question or comment from the man was unusual, so he proactively visited to make sure things were going smoothly.

Osaigbovo just cocked his head, a puzzled expression painted across his face. "Oh," he said. "Mr. Wayman said that…"

Matthew's interest was piqued, so he urged him to continue.

The man shook his head and flashed his teeth in an apologetic cringe. "Sah, Mr. Wayman said that I should report to him."

He had to stop himself from exclaiming, covering his shock with a laugh. "He must need more training, then," Matthew joked, hoping his laughter was enough to disarm the situation.

As he walked away, anger twisted heavy in his gut. He'd noticed even before that exchange that Wayman seemed disinterested in speaking with him, a hard turn from his former boss who would stop by to chat several times a day. Matthew had assumed his new boss was simply unfriendly. After all, Matthew had always been widely known and respected as the smartest, most qualified worker at the plant—there was no reason to believe a new boss would change that.

Or at least that was what he assumed until that September. He sauntered into the managerial meeting, his mind rattling through the list of tasks he needed to complete by the end of the day. As he glanced around the table, he couldn't seem to make eye contact with the other five staff members. One wrote endlessly in his notebook and another picked at his cuticles. In stark contrast to the friendly atmosphere these meetings usually had—at least back when Hariprasad was in charge—the room radiated an unusual, eerie quiet that raised the hair on his arms.

The last few meetings had been strained—not to this degree, but certainly uncomfortable. About a month earlier, he'd noticed strange trends in hiring. Not only was Wayman hiring more workers, despite profit increases that were negligible at best—but Matthew had noticed that the new employees he met weren't from Rivers State. At first, he'd tried to brush it off—maybe other indigenes had been hired, and he just hadn't met them yet.

When he raised the issue in the management meeting, Wayman had brushed him off, citing multi-million-naira growth over the previous five-month period, and explaining that such monumental success necessitated the hiring of the company's 140 new employees.

Matthew saw no evidence to support that position.

So he poked around a bit more. What he learned was beyond alarming. Not only had Osaigbovo and Wayman brought more new employees on board than revenue could support, they'd also implemented a six-fold increase in hires from Bendel State. Those hires were being assigned primarily to supervisory roles, while Rivers State hires were almost exclusively hired as junior employees.

Realizing that problems that could arise from these unjustifiable hiring decisions—chiefly accusations of fraud and abuse—he'd raised the issue in the second August managers' meeting with a gentle reminder to funnel hires through the Personnel Department.

He realized with a sunken heart that he'd also raised the issue in his meeting with the commissioner when he and Wayman presented their report. As the strange, tense silence in the room continued to fester, he feared he'd gone too far in sharing the concerns with Commissioner Obowu.

Wayman cleared his throat, signaling the opening of the September meeting, the wet sound hanging in the air. Flipping open his leather folio, he barked, "Let's begin, shall we?"

As business proceeded as usual, Matthew began to relax. Perhaps he'd misread the room—after all, everything seemed as it should be. The administrations manager requested an update—from Wayman, he noticed, rather than from him—on the hiring of several new employees. The factory floor manager raised the issue of an aging machine, which Matthew jotted down for later reference.

But when he looked up from his notes, Wayman was glaring at him.

Matthew just stared back.

Quickly averting his gaze, Wayman said, "We will need to investigate the uniform issue." At that, he looked Matthew straight in the eye. "Mamah, I'm putting you on forced leave while we complete the investigation."

His mind reeling, he coughed out a weak, "What?"

"It's not a request," the man sneered. "It's an order."

Charismatic and charming, he'd never had much trouble endearing himself to others. Now, he was being disciplined—investigated, even—and in front of his peers. The thought propelled him forward. "Why?" he asked, his tone bolder and more confident. "What did I do?"

"As you well know, company policy is to accept the lowest bid."

Matthew blinked, searching his memory for any clue that could illuminate Wayman's point. "Of course," he said.

Despite Matthew's best efforts to stare the man down—if he was going to ambush him like this, the least he could do was look him in the eye—Wayman buried his eyes in the collection of documents in front of him.

When the man looked up, a trace of a smirk showed at the corner of his mouth. "You've accepted an abnormally high bid from your friend, uh—" he rifled through the pages, "Dagogo, is it?" He flipped the folio shut, and propped his elbow on the table, staring at him once more.

At the man's dismissive, condescending tone, Matthew's mind raced. He'd taken five bids and selected the lowest. As was policy, he had priced out the uniforms and submitted the lowest proposal to accounting, who would issue a purchase order, finalizing the supplier contract.

It was the most ordinary process in the world. He'd done it this time, as always, in the most ordinary way.

"Why didn't you tell me about this earlier?" Matthew asked, vacillating between perplexed and defensive. Bringing up the issue during a staff meeting was unheard of—to add a verbal, undocumented notification of forced leave far exceeded the realm of anything Matthew had seen at WAGI or elsewhere. Matthew seethed through the meeting's conclusion, through their dismissal, on his way to his office, then home. By the time he walked through the door, he had a well-rehearsed letter in mind. Barely pausing to greet the family, he grabbed a stack of paper, plopped down on the yellow felt sofa surrounded by framed family pictures on the wall, and scrawled a lengthy screed to the commissioner detailing the laundry list of Wayman's bad behavior and dangerous managerial tactics.

Perhaps the action was too strong. He didn't care. For more than two months, he'd endured dismissal and disregard from the man. For more than two months, he'd put up with the factory manager going over his head. For more than two months, he'd watched the company change around him from a business he'd been proud to serve to one that seemed intent on cutting out high-level workers from the very region that supported its existence. And now he was being suspended for no good reason.

His people deserved more. He deserved more.

Without a trace of regret, he dropped the letter in the mail.

Perhaps, while he waited for the commissioner's response, he could at least make the most of time with his family.

Even that seemed to fall flat. As the second and third day of his forced leave ticked by, he found himself continually irritated. With every whine, every sibling disagreement or playtime screech, he felt his own irritability lurking behind his eyes, ready to pounce.

The fourth day brought merciful relief. In a letter delivered to his home, Wayman invited him to return to the office. Cautiously optimistic—but still deeply suspicious of this insecure, threatening little man—Matthew made his way to work the next day.

As he walked into the management meeting, the tension once again vibrated around him. Everyone seemed on edge, and he couldn't shake the feeling that this man—this graying, overly confident, imposter of a manager—would somehow find a way to ruin him.

"I have convened this meeting mainly to discuss the allegations contained in the letter dated 7 September, from Mamah to the Commissioner," Wayman said sternly.

At the sound of his name, Matthew's blood ran cold.

Before he could object, Wayman handed a thin packet of papers to Osaigbovo. Then another to the man next to him, and one to the man on his right. Finally, he extended a copy of the document to Matthew.

Dear Commissioner, it read in his own sharp, precise handwriting.

"Despite the fact that our Assistant General Manager agreed to take vacation while we sorted the issue of the uniforms," Wayman began, peering at Matthew over his reading glasses, "And, despite the fact that he admitted his inexperience in management, and that he is not prepared to handle the factory's affairs—"

"I did not say that!" Matthew exclaimed.

But Wayman charged ahead. "—our fellow employee has written to the commissioner with some quite serious allegations."

Matthew opened his mouth to protest, but Wayman didn't even pause for breath.

"If as Mamah suggests," he boomed, "there was an alarming increase in the employee recruitment, he should have pointed it out at previous meetings."

"But I had no knowledge! I did not take part in all aspects of recruitment, but for one occasion!"

Wayman leaned against the table. "Mamah!" he said, raising his voice. "I want you to answer a question! Are you still interested in performing as a member of the management team?"

Swallowing hard, Matthew looked Wayman in the eye. He willed himself, now, to speak slowly and deliberately. "I would only work with a management team that is disciplined and unbia—"

"Mamah!" Wayman roared. "It's a simple question! Can you continue to work here in a productive manner?!"

"I have always worked relentlessly towards achieving the objectives of the company," Matthew asserted. "Always!"

"Do not raise your voice to me!" Wayman wailed. "We're done here!"

Stomping out the conference room door, the man looked awkward and dangerous. Other attendees silently gathered their things. They wandered out of the room as Matthew sat, confused and upset, processing what had happened.

He wasn't sure how long he'd been sitting there—no more

than a few minutes—when a petite woman in a green dress crept timidly into the room.

"Dr. Mamah," she said. "*Oga* said that I should give this to you."

Without another word, Matthew ripped open the letter. He read the lines once, then again, and finally a third time before he stuffed it back in its envelope. Then, as slowly and confidently as he could, he walked through the conference room door, down the hall, and out the door of the building.

Like any fire, the rage in his gut threatened to swallow everything in its path.

But fire could also be harnessed. And, if it took everything he had, he would not burn.

Chapter 18

NIGERWIVES

⸺

A CONSTANT VIGIL OF WORRY SHROUDED Judit's life. Like the black, slithering serpent that once inched toward her kitchen door, a shadowy tension seemed to follow Matthew home from work, replacing the stress of fussy newborns with an ominous question—how would they raise five children if they lost their only source of income?

There must have been a time before she worried so much. Before the first twins were born, perhaps, or maybe in her late thirties. No matter how she tried to recall that time, to relax her shoulders and loosen her jaw, the difficulties of the current situation wrapped around her, squeezing the breath from her lungs.

She tried to remind herself of their good fortune—surely not everything was bad. The children were doing well. Even when they came down with a little cough—or asthma, in Tonye's case—they were mostly healthy. Many people would have traded their lives for happy, thriving children.

But, as the WAGI tensions escalated, she struggled to juggle her responsibilities as the children's mother and Matthew's wife.

Neither of them had any real sense of what Wayman could do—could he get Matthew fired? Could he keep him from getting another job? Could he ruin his entire career?

The questions seared hot in Judit's mind, but she tried to push them away. His face a mixture of anger and humiliation, she had no idea how to comfort him—how to support someone who must feel emasculated and small—but she knew the answer didn't lie in more questions.

So she threw her arms around him, nuzzling her nose into his neck and stroking his cheek. At first, he seemed to resist, his body stiff and tense, but he finally relaxed into her, crumpling in a defeat she hadn't felt from him before.

They stood like that for some time, until she heard the padding of little footsteps behind her, "Apu…" Ebinimi said as she entered.

In an instant, Matthew resumed his former height—his former pride—and greeted their daughter before making his way out to settle a minor scuffle with the boys over how much bread to eat.

Judit watched as he left, her mind reeling with the news.

They'd been barely scraping by as it was—that was part of the reason they'd been so intent on Matthew stepping into Hariprasad's role. The extra income would have helped to support the five growing children, all of whom seemed to eat more every day.

Since Wayman began at WAGI, Judit had already noticed Matthew bringing stress home from the office, complaining constantly about the unfair treatment, even as the two struggled to care for the children.

That was nothing compared to this. Scrimping by on his salary as it stood, they had almost nothing saved. A fifty-percent reduction in his salary could destroy them. He would fight it, that much was certain.

How, she had no idea.

And alongside him, she would fight to keep the family cared for.

They had begun to ration their food. Without much in storage, they needed to make the food they had last.

Like everything else they'd been through, they would come out of this struggle stronger than before.

The first week, she'd felt confident—even defiant. Though the situation was far from ideal, she would make it work—they would make it work together. She stretched their meals with grains she had on hand and thanked God that she was still producing plenty of breast milk for the babies.

The second week was harder. The pantry grains had diminished to dust on the shelf, and buying food at the market became more frustrating than ever. Pegging her a wealthy "oyibo," sellers demanded higher prices from her than from others, sometimes almost harassing her for money she didn't have. She wanted to scream at them—I have five children and no money, no food!—but she swallowed her pride and pushed for the best prices she could.

As the weeks ticked by—three, then four, then five—the situation grew even more dire.

She'd never dreamed that this half-salary suspension would continue this long.

Now, she could only stare at the bare pantry, her stomach turning in a mixture of dread and frustration. She tried to keep the family's spirits up, reminding the children that they still had food—they just had to eat a little less. One piece of meat was better than none, after all! And they could still enjoy eggs! They just had to cut them in half—it was great practice in sharing!

But as her own hunger threatened to bore through her stomach, she felt her grip on the situation slipping.

Then, like a miracle, life handed her something unexpected. Two long weeks after he'd been suspended, Matthew had gone before the board to discuss the issues he saw in the company. He'd written to the commissioner about these issues before, but all that had come of it was a suspension. Now, he told her with a twinkle of hope finally returning to his eyes, he would address the commissioner about these issues with Wayman present. The man would finally have to answer for his cruelty!

The night before the meeting, she'd pulled together all the food she could spare to prepare a full meal—Matthew would need his strength.

He hardly touched his food. When she asked him how the meeting went, he gave a measured response. She could appreciate that—after all, surely both had learned to be cautious of future planning.

Hour by hour, she waited, one day rolling into the next, tension churning and the roar of her empty stomach as she felt the tiny sliver of promise melt away.

And then, one afternoon, he'd burst in holding a newspaper. "They are talking about us in the papers!" he exclaimed.

Cautious but eager, she'd taken the paper from him. There it was, in huge, bold, black letters as the front-page headline of the September 25 issue of the *Nigerian Tide*:

"CRISIS AT THE GLASS FACTORY." And in smaller letters, "Government orders probe."

It seemed the press was on their side. The company was being investigated for Wayman's practices, and the article seemed sympathetic to the company's lack of Nigerian leadership in favor of expatriates.

A small-framed sub header on the page read: "2 weeks to submit report." Judit wondered, could it be true? That in just two weeks a report would be submitted? Of course, It wouldn't promise an end to the problem, but it was a ray of hope that things were moving forward.

She'd hugged Matthew then with a force that threatened to knock him off his feet. But soon they were quieted, the fatigue of hunger settling into their bones.

She saw it in the kids' drawn faces, too.

Tonye had always been thin, and a picky eater. But her poor Obi had been bigger and his clothes began to hang off him. Ebinimi looked gaunt.

She thought she would never experience something so devastating. As week six turned to week seven, she knew she was wrong.

She also felt her milk drying up as she sacrificed her own nourishment for her older children.

"I'm not hungry," she would say, affecting cheerfulness in her voice. "The three of you, share my bread!"

But she was hungry.

She started to feel dizzy at times and distracted, her mind constantly cycling through thoughts of food, fantasies of what she would eat if she could eat anything at all.

Week eight became week nine. Shortly after the newspaper article, Matthew had been officially reinstated by WAGI's board, but still, Wayman refused to honor their wishes. When he'd been told that his back pay would be restored, making up for the lost money, she allowed herself to hope—just a bit—that things would be okay.

But that was weeks ago, and no check had arrived.

Neither was Matthew allowed back at work.

After days of worry, she would fall into bed, only to find she couldn't sleep, her brain wide awake and her pelvic bones digging into the mattress, pinching the increasingly crepey skin that sagged slightly around her hips.

And as she lay there, sleepless but exhausted, her mind flickered to her parents' stories. They'd often recounted times when they didn't have enough to eat—when no one had enough of anything. Without access to flour, they'd run whole wheat through a coffee grinder. Her mother had been able to buy yeast—a rare treat during Communist rule—and had combined it with the half-ground grain to make bread.

It wasn't ideal, of course. Much of the wheat peel remained, making the bread grainy, but it was all they had. To think of it now, Judit thought it sounded like a delicacy—that must have been how the family had felt back then, too.

To stretch the little brick of bread, her mother had put together a dip of peas and onions, toasted in oil, and soon after, everyone in the family fell ill. Most had to have their stomachs pumped.

Later, they'd learned that the new store on Ulászló Street, where her mother had purchased the oil, had replaced cooking oil with engine oil. In a moment of such extreme, widespread poverty, even a little treat of bread and dip could turn dangerous—threatening everything you had.

The story had always rung horrible in her ears, but she realized now that she hadn't understood what her mother had gone through. Not really.

Now that she was also a mother of five children faced with the gnawing inability to feed and care for them, now that she stared down a future that seemed less certain than anything she'd experienced as an adult—now, she thought she understood.

The memory—horrible enough in the past—settled over her, a buried history fighting its way into her family's future.

Whatever came their way, as long as the family was safe, she could handle it. A person could endure much more than they thought—if her mother's stories of war proved anything, it was that.

She'd been about Marika and Terike's age when her mother had held her on her lap, huddled in the back seat of the farm's only automobile, a black, two-door model—very novel at the time—and fled to Budapest. Having waited as long as they could—through radio declarations of an advancing Russian front and a friend's warning that they could hear cannon fire from their homes—the time had finally come. The carriages were loaded with food and belongings, coachmen were hired, and her mother and the children had left her father behind, praying for safety. Judit's father had paid the drivers a larger sum than they could afford because they feared transporting the family would result in detainment by the incoming Russian soldiers.

She thought of how her mother must have felt, fear lurching in her stomach—just as hunger now churned in hers—as the children climbed excitedly into the car. She thought her mother must have allowed her siblings the peace of ignorance as long as possible. Perhaps she'd even encouraged the children's excitement.

If the trip had gone as planned, she suspected she wouldn't have heard so many stories.

But it hadn't. Like her family's current situation, those stories seemed to layer one horror after another, until the anxiety had become a part of her.

Her sister recalled the trip vividly. After proceeding uneventfully from Szöllős, they were nearing the Tisza River when the driver suddenly screeched to a halt. Clad in an olive green military jacket with prominent pockets and leather strappings, a soldier strolled to the car's window in his high black leather boots.

Her sisters remembered his clothing.

All her mother remembered was the gun.

Judit couldn't imagine what that must have been like. What would she have done in that situation? Her mother had been solely responsible for the safety of the children. Since her father had stayed behind—waiting to join them later—her mother had only the driver to protect them. She shuddered to think of it.

The soldier had let them go—it would have been unusual for a German soldier to harm Hungarians—but after dropping the family off at their hosts' house in Dabas, the driver had stolen their car.

Still, they'd made it to Budapest, packed into a horse and carriage courtesy of Uncle Bandi, Albert's older brother. Just a baby at the time, Judit had no memory of the events. But the trauma had shaped the whole family—their perspectives reshaped by the threat of death.

The same couldn't be said of her family now, and she thanked God for that.

As the family ticked toward their third month of hunger, she began to question that assumption. Terrible things happened to starving people—she'd seen it in Nigerian villages—and she was starting to experience more severe weakness.

Were her children feeling it too? What lasting damage could come from malnutrition?

Through it all, she couldn't shake the cruelty, how her brilliant, kind, energetic husband had been nearing the pinnacle of the company one day and in the next, plunged into indescribable hopelessness.

Every time they'd received good news—the board took his side, the commissioner supported him, the press was intervening—Matthew's boss somehow found a way to maintain the family's suffering. Every time a glimmer of respite appeared, Wayman savagely wiped it away.

She was afraid to hope.

So she prayed.

After three months without enough to eat—three months of the gnawing pangs of hunger in her belly as she gave up her food to feed the children—prayer was all she had left.

In Nigerian confessionals, it wasn't unusual to share your problems as well as your sins. She appreciated that, at least. As comforting as it was to unburden herself to the priest, the visits weren't enough to ease her fear.

They weren't enough to make her feel less lonely—more supported.

Until, one day, she heard a knock at the door.

"Judit," the woman said, her British accent crisp and bright. "It's so good to see you!"

She remembered the woman from years earlier—when they'd first moved to Port Harcourt, Judy Nwanodi had stopped by their blue Rumuobiakani house. While she hadn't stayed in touch as much as she would have liked, Judit had deeply appreciated the warm welcome. Judy held citizenship in both the United States and England but had immigrated to Port Harcourt in the 50s. Like Judit, she was a thin woman with brown hair, except sparkling blue eyes peeked out under her bangs.

Now, as they sat in the Mamah living room, Judit felt grateful for the community.

"I would normally ask if you wanted some tea," she told the woman sheepishly. "I'm afraid we're out." She felt herself blush a bit. "I haven't had a chance to—"

"Oh, don't worry, dear," the older woman comforted her. "I can't stay long—I'm just making my rounds to the immigrant wives in the area."

Judit gave her a puzzled expression.

"Have you ever heard of Nigerwives?"

She hadn't, but as Judy explained the group to her—made up of immigrant women married to Nigerians who had moved to Nigeria, the group had branches around the country, providing activities and support for its members—she was intrigued.

The group, Judy said, could be a place of their own. Something they build together, with their husbands' support, but without depending on them.

Well, as the woman explained, leaning in conspiratorially, *usually* the women had their husbands' support. "Some of the men don't like us getting together."

Judit nodded, familiar with this way of thinking and grateful that Matthew had never made her feel this way.

"But you and I know—we women have our own issues to think about!"

"Yes!" Judit exclaimed, her head spinning with ideas for the group—maybe she could start a library or teach music classes to the children. They could spend family evenings together—the kids could play and the adults could enjoy conversation. There were so many possibilities! Of course, it would be a bit before she'd have the energy to participate so much, but perhaps it was a step towards getting her family on their feet again.

"I'm glad you agree. It's high time we started a group in Rivers State!"

When Judy left, Judit eagerly scrawled the first meeting date in her calendar. They would meet once a month to start, but, as the woman explained, they could sometimes meet for other special events as needed.

She'd felt a deep longing for friendship since they'd moved to Port Harcourt, but it was only when she heard of the group that she realized how badly she needed to be around others who understood what she was going through. Though she'd made acquaintances of a few other foreign women in the area, she still felt she had no one to relate to more deeply. Matthew had lived in Port Harcourt. He innately understood the various cultures in Rivers State. While she felt she had adjusted well enough, she would always be faced with the challenges of being an immigrant.

It was a spot of relief amid the most challenging time of her life, a time that demanded so much sacrifice with so little reward.

With something to look forward to, maybe the days wouldn't be quite as long—maybe there was room to dream.

As it turned out, there really was.

One afternoon, Matthew came home with news. Wayman had been ordered by the board to reinstall him in the company. The "Wayman War," as she'd begun to call it, was ending.

She felt sure of it.

Chapter 19

GOVERNOR

~

NEW YEAR'S EVE, 1984 IN Nigeria marked a
year of rule by Major General Muhammadu Buhari,
following another military coup. Buhari claimed to
have taken over the country to focus on issues of corruption, and
shortly after his installment, he'd gathered many of the country's
most powerful leaders, asking for their advice and support. While
coups of any kind were unsettling, Matthew agreed with many
of the leaders' contentions. The new government's promises were
two-fold: they would promote economic austerity, and they would
crack down on corruption in the public sector.

Actions had been taken to this end. As Buhari promised, corrupt government officials were immediately jailed. That shift, most
could agree, was a step in the right direction. However, some of
the tactics appeared not to be based on policy, but on the whims
of military officials. Public employees who came late to work were
sometimes ordered by soldiers to do "frog jumps," a punishment
designed to humiliate workers and ensure that government time
was used efficiently and well.

Matthew had seen more corruption than ever before. WAGI seemed to be spiraling, and, no matter what he did to stop it, things got worse—both for the company and for him.

After his long absence and multiple orders, Wayman finally allowed Matthew to report for duty. His first day back would be December 31, 1984.

Earlier in the whole fiasco, the invitation to return would have been a relief, but he'd been through the woods with Wayman. He knew better than to trust this man. It had been a long time in the works, with Wayman fighting him at every turn—in fact, the board had clearly ordered the Managing Director to reinstate Matthew three weeks earlier.

Wayman had refused, replying with a slate of newly-fabricated complaints against Matthew, each more ridiculous than the last. He'd argued that Matthew should be removed from the company entirely and incorrectly informed the board that he'd been receiving his full salary despite the suspension.

It seemed Matthew couldn't catch a break.

His salary had been ordered repaid, that part was true, but they had yet to receive a check.

If that wasn't evidence enough of Wayman's unhinged behavior, he'd also paid a visit to one of WAGI's collaborating companies. With his wife in tow, he'd visited the General Manager there— rumor had it that Wayman's wife had told Elsie, in a threatening voice, "We know who your friends are." She'd even mentioned Matthew by name, implying that Elsie should not associate with him.

Matthew would have laughed at the ludicrous situation if not for the real threat Wayman posed. After all, the man had already cost the family months of nourishment. Who knew what else he could do to impact not only Matthew's current job, but his future career prospects, too.

Matthew was suspicious of how things would materialize. He strongly suspected that the battle wasn't yet over.

As they'd rationed their food, he'd seen Judit give up her own portions for the children. Obi's appetite had always been larger than the others, making him seem to suffer especially. He would sometimes ingest toothpaste or cough syrup to quell his hunger, a realization that made Matthew equally sad and furious.

Matthew found himself increasingly frustrated at his lack of power over the situation. After years of education and hard work, he deeply resented the family's struggles. The tensions that surrounded his efforts to resolve the situation layered on top of his own gnawing hunger made him increasingly irritable.

He knew he sometimes took out his frustration on the family. Tonye's former academic excellence was waning. Now more than ever, Matthew realized the importance of education and could not stand by while his child slacked in his studies. Perhaps, under different circumstances, he wouldn't have felt corporal punishment necessary. But tensions were high, and feeling the lack of control spread into every aspect of his life, he punished his son with a flogging—and he made Tonye repeat his freshman year for a third time.

The battle at work affected more than just his family—and more than just his own career.

All of Nigeria was harmed by the wave of corruption, by the preference of expats over indigenes. Rivers State was harmed by Wayman's determination to replace qualified workers from the Riverine region with Bendelites.

The entire incident had begun because Wayman had no respect for Matthew's work, despite his doctorate, despite his previous commendations, and despite his dedicated labor. While he couldn't prove it, he couldn't help but believe that the Managing Director's hostility had been a direct result of Matthew's high-achieving, charismatic personality. Something Wayman distinctly lacked.

Wayman had been out to get him since they'd first met—he was sure of it—not only aiming to unseat him from his current position but, now, to force him out of the company entirely.

That sense of being hunted had hung around him like a fog, blocking his vision and, more than anything, proving a constant source of frustration.

Such a long period of uncertainty—after the Board had ruled in his favor, but before Wayman accepted their ruling—added an additional layer of instability. It boggled his mind to think of how a single man could prevent his life from moving forward, and out of no other reason than spite. Even worse, his entire family had been suffering at the hands of one man.

Public sentiment had collected on his side—he was glad for that at least. Not only had allegations arisen noting that the Director had improperly purchased multiple new vehicles against company policy, the numbers of new employees he was hiring were shocking. Matthew had pointed this out in the fall when the new employee rate rose by thirty percent. Since then, the poor use of company funds had accelerated—and people were finally starting to notice.

Between this and the insubordination demonstrated by Wayman's refusal to reinstate Matthew, it was hard to see why the man remained in Nigeria at all. After all, WAGI was still a state-owned company.

The board had explicitly ordered Wayman to reinstate Matthew on December 10.

By the following week, the Managing Director had done nothing but try to dredge up more false accusations against Matthew.

Then a second week came and went, and he heard a rumor that the Director had gone on vacation.

Finally, halfway through the third week, he received a letter from Wayman, asking him to return to work.

With a trepidation beyond anything he'd experienced, he made his way to work on December 31, the first day he was to report back. Much to his surprise, the hours passed without incident, and he returned home to an encouraging, supportive Judit.

But on the third day, he received the letter he'd feared. It looked, on its surface, like any other company memo. After a brief request for explanation, a list of the previous year's expenses was attached, primarily including the company-approved expenditures for furniture in the family home. That familiar hot rage rose again in his chest.

He'd been given forty-eight hours to respond.

As he sat down to complete the form the next day at work, he received a second memo.

"Dear Dr. Mamah," it read. "By this letter, you are suspended from duty with this company. You are to leave the company premises immediately and not return until further advised."

His entire body vibrated with injustice. After starving his family for months, this man was again baring his teeth, his barely masked aggression threatening to overtake Matthew. Fighting against his instinct to crumple the letter into a ball, he instead laid the paper down and took out two fresh sheets.

He addressed the first to Wayman, following protocol—as he always did—of appealing the suspension, and he addressed the second to the Chairman of the Board. It took everything he had not to march, screaming, into his office.

That same day—January 4—the Board's Chair wrote to the Military Governor of Rivers State, Police Commissioner Fidelis Oyakhilome, detailing the issues Matthew had faced and asking for an intervention.

The letter also called for Wayman's removal.

By mid-February, not only was the man still managing the plant—he'd gone on a major hiring spree, populating the company with more and more non-indigenous workers.

Matthew was done waiting for the government to intervene.

In March, he was offered a new government job. Much to Judit's delight, his name was scrawled across newspapers even before he'd officially been confirmed for the job. Matthew would be the General Manager of Waterglass Boatyard Limited, another public company that manufactured boats and small ships. Matthew would oversee methods for improving the quality of glass-reinforced fibers for building boats.

The salary was meager compared to that of other General Managers, and well below what he'd hoped to make if he'd moved up the chain at WAGI as he should have. But, as problems with Wayman continued to escalate, the company had begun the process of privatization.

At least, as a public employee, he was provided with free medical care for the family, furnished housing, and a company car. Basic home repairs were also included as a benefit, and he was assigned a security guard and a house girl.

He appreciated the stability the role provided. Even after Matthew was reassigned, he continued to follow the drama at WAGI.

As investigations continued, the government uncovered more and more improprieties. Some of these issues had been raised by Matthew for a long time. Others were well beyond the scope of his knowledge. For example, Wayman had used company funds reserved for buying a forklift to buy a Range Rover for his private use. He'd also used company funds to free an expatriate friend apprehended at the airport with hemp.

Another month passed before Wayman finally wrote in his own defense, and the man inexplicably complained about his own unfair treatment. He claimed his wife was unlawfully taken from his house, in front of their children, by Immigration Officers, in an attempt to force him to leave Port Harcourt.

It was ironic to hear Wayman complaining about unfair actions taken against his family, when Matthew had watched his own family suffering—his wife going hungry, his growing sons wasting away, and his daughters' cheeks turning hollow.

For years—nearly his whole life—he'd been striving to make a difference. He consistently strove for excellence, pushing his family, friends, and workers to do the same.

Why couldn't he be the one to push Rivers State in that direction, too? Why couldn't he lead the government to greatness?

He was a charismatic public speaker—people told him that often—and the people in his village all but praised him as a celebrity when he went home. He was clearly admired by the people of Rivers State, and he doubted anyone had a greater knowledge of Nigerian politics and history than he.

He shook off the idea.

It was probably silly.

For now, he needed to focus on his new job. Perhaps one day he could make a difference in his country, just like he'd imagined he would when he was in college in Port Harcourt.

For now, he would find a way to be content making a difference at home.

Chapter 20

NOTES AND STAVES

J UDIT HAD NEVER BEEN ONE to obsess over material wealth. Even as a child, she knew—it wasn't money that made a person happy. It was love.

So when her family didn't have everything they wanted, she reminded them to focus on what they did have. They had good relationships with one another, she and Matthew's marriage was relatively solid, and the children were all mentally and physically strong.

As long as they had their health and happiness, nothing else mattered.

The "Wayman War" had been a stern reminder of that. And now that it was over, they could focus on the important things.

Even so, Judit wanted more. As much as she'd wanted a family when she married Matthew—that was her life's calling—she'd also hoped to work a paying job at some point.

When the idea came up to start a family company—the two of them, Judit and Matthew—she embraced it. They called it JUMA Global Nigeria Limited, the acronym derived from the initial letters of their names. It had a broad focus but primarily included the import and export of goods and general contracting. As the operation materialized, their excitement only grew—from wholesale spaghetti to gas cookers, wood carvings to water heaters, and even fruit and shark fins, the sales ideas went on and on.

Matthew couldn't be the company's official leader—public employees were barred from taking on such roles. While Judit would serve as the Executive Director, she remained cognizant of her responsibilities to the family. The boys and Ebinimi were older, but far from self-sufficient, and, of course, Marika and Terike still fully depended on her.

In truth, she realized now that managing the household would always be a hefty job. Nigeria also still perplexed her. The phrase "NEPA took light!"—meaning that the power was out—continued to ring out on a regular basis, and they couldn't afford a generator. Sometimes the water ran out, and they would have to fetch more using large jerrycans.

All clothing had to be hand-washed and air-dried, which had seemed fine when she was a child. But it was the 80s now, and many Europeans she knew at least had electric washers. Of course, those wouldn't do much good when NEPA took light, but she longed for the ease that would come with such machines. If she never had to handwash the children's clothes, she could accomplish so much more!

There was much more she wanted to accomplish.

To be "just a housewife" could be disheartening—it made her question her future. After all, she had a graduate degree. She was highly educated and, at one time, had a fair amount of work experience.

Back then, she hadn't realized that the experience would serve her well as a mother, too—managing a household of seven was not for the faint of heart! She occasionally found herself stressed, swallowing her frustration until it slipped out. From time to time, she snapped at her children for transgressions that later seemed minor, even silly. She always recalled those moments with a sting of shame, and that only compounded her stress.

It was difficult to process those feelings alone. While she had Miriam and Rosemarie—Nigerwives she had gratefully befriended—she never felt she could burden others with her negative feelings. She always listened and offered advice for others' most difficult challenges. It didn't matter how long she'd known them—she found it fulfilling to support others.

Things weren't so bad. She knew she should be grateful for all she had.

But it was clear that she could not run a company on her own—and even with Matthew doing most of the acquisitions work, they would need outside assistance to make sure JUMA ran smoothly. A commercial manager, perhaps, would be an excellent role—someone who could visit with Port Harcourt sellers and liaise with foreign business partners by telegram, securing buyers for their various wholesale products.

They hired a sales representative to help ensure JUMA's success—after all, neither Matthew nor Judit could spend as much time as the company required—and it gave Judit more time with family.

Not just her husband and children, but also her parents and siblings back in Hungary.

Trips home always provided a well-needed time to relax. As six of the Mamahs flooded through the familiar threshold of the Zsombolyai apartment—Matthew would join them later—her heart swelled at the thought of reuniting her children with their grandparents, aunts, uncles, and cousins.

They loved their Hungarian family, particularly when Aunt Bori came through the door proffering a new cake she baked. She was a good cook, often inviting the family over for meals. On a trip in 1985, Judit got to spend time with Peter Bartók and his girlfriend, Hope, as well.

Peter was the younger son of Béla Bartók, though he didn't resemble his famous father, with dark brown hair, a rounded face, and a graying goatee, as much as his brother did. He had immigrated to the United States in his early adulthood and served in the United States Navy. As a young boy, he often spent his summers with Judit's parents in Szöllős. Though he now lived very far away, he remained in touch and very fond of the Koós family.

"You're very thin," he said, his expression startled. Stepping back from her, he furrowed his brow.

In the crisp, Hungarian air, she'd almost forgotten the troubles back home, the difficult years they'd struggled beneath the weight of suspensions and missing paychecks, on top of the typical challenges of life.

She preferred it that way, a welcome distraction.

She shrugged off Peter's comment—others in her family had said the same thing—and gave a weak smile.

Awkward as it was, observations like his were an excellent excuse to indulge in an extra helping of the foods she'd missed while she was away—the rich spices of hearty Hungarian meals.

It felt good to have her stomach full.

Her heart was full, too.

As the children sat with her father, they radiated joy. She sensed that what her children loved most—even more than trips to the amusement park or zoo—was spending time with family.

They adored their grandparents.

When they were little, their grandfather would walk with them to the "bottomless pond"—a small park near the house with a little body of water that, of course, wasn't actually bottomless—to feed the ducks. While the activity itself was fun, what they really loved was the ice cream he spoiled them with on their way back.

They enjoyed his stories. One of the boy's favorites was about Miklós Toldi, a legendary nobleman in Hungarian folklore, who was so physically powerful he could subdue wolves with his bare hands.

He was so tender with them—loving and gentle, though often sterner than their grandmother—that one could almost forget all he'd been through. At one time, she'd thought he must be nearly as strong as Toldi himself. Now, watching him with her children, she saw the folds and lines in his face, the residue of laughter and love alongside the shadows of pain and fear. He was telling her children the nightmare that had been her first birthday, a day she didn't remember but a story she knew well.

Her first birthday had marked the cessation of active combat, as the city surrendered to the Allies following the Siege of Budapest. The casualties—both in human lives and the city's beautiful historic structures—had been catastrophic.

Amid the death and destruction, as the family reeled to process what had happened, a knock came at the door.

"Albert Koós!" a deep male voice declared. Heavily accented, the voice badly mispronounced his name. The aggressive pounding made the message clear. "Albert Koós! *Vykhodi bystro!*" another voice repeated, "Come out!"

As her father told it, he'd recognized the situation immediately. The Soviets were taking people, thousands of Hungarian civilians, as prisoners of war. Given his military accolades from the previous

World War, her father was an easy target, a man unlikely to support communism the way the Russians expected.

The Soviets had burst through their door and handcuffed him, robbing the family of even a precious few moments for hugs, kisses, and farewells.

They'd known that they may never see him again. The trauma was scrawled across her siblings' faces when they recounted the story. It made Judit grateful that she couldn't remember the terrible moment.

But, as her mother often told them, her father had stayed calm, steadfast in his determination. "I am alright," he reassured them. "Things could always be worse."

He couldn't have believed that—at least not with any certainty.

As he, along with hundreds of others, was loaded into a cargo wagon, he must have doubted his words. They'd been taken to the basement of the five-floor V-shaped building at the corner of Fadrusz and Miklós Horthy streets. The latter street would later be renamed in honor of Béla Bartók, a tragic irony considering the circumstances. For two days, the prisoners were held there, denied access even to the most basic sanitation until the basement became horrendously filthy, reeking of urine, feces, and despair.

Her father recounted trekking east in a compact formation. When they reached the Premontrei Secondary School, a campus of four buildings surrounding a large, rectangular open space, the Soviets had ushered them into classrooms for the night.

A man among them had gotten an idea, her father told the family, a sly glint in his eye.

The abandoned school afforded many opportunities, its spaces packed with pencils and books—the only tools they needed for communication.

"THEY HAVE TAKEN ME TO GÖDÖLLŐ," he'd written on a torn page. "I AM ALRIGHT." Scrawled below the message was his name and, on the other side, his wife's name along with the family address. He'd crumpled the note and jammed it into his pocket.

When they were moved from the school, he discreetly threw the note on the ground, optimistic that existing national solidarity would shepherd it to its destination. The prisoners, meanwhile, were corralled and taken by train to a camp in Cegléd, with many growing weak and emaciated. From there, most would go eastward to the Soviet Union where they would be assigned to work in forced labor camps.

Despite his promise to his family, her father feared he wouldn't make it if things came to that.

When he told the story, the children would lean forward on the edge of their seats.

"What did you do, *Nagyapa*?!"

The answer was simple and ingenious. By adding a small circle to his required documents, he'd turned his birth year from 1899 to 1889, making him appear fifty-six years old—too old for the work camps.

With his prematurely graying hair, he'd always looked older than his age. His face had grown weathered and gray-stubbled due to the poor conditions, making him look even older.

For once, he'd thought, this could be an advantage.

His plan had worked! Tired and weak, but finally released from captivity, he'd stared down a fifty-mile trek back to Budapest, a fifteen-hour trip in the best conditions. In his deteriorated state, it took weeks.

Finally, on April 18, he reunited with his family. His children's prayers had been answered.

As such a young child then, Judit couldn't remember the relief. But she'd heard it recounted all her life.

And now, seeing her father with her children, she shuddered to think of how things could have ended. She thanked God he'd escaped.

He'd slipped into the comfortable role of grandfather, worn in by her nieces and nephews well before her children were born, and his stern yet playful mannerisms were a hit with the boys in particular.

Some days, he'd show them the "goodness stick" that hung on his bedroom wall.

"I will use it to beat the unruly children," he playfully warned them, a twinkle in his eye.

Of course, he would never do such a thing—and the children knew it—but he loved to joke with them. He'd use the same teasing tone when he showed them his whip, a relic from his equestrian days.

While he would never joke about them, he showed the boys his weapons, too. Back in Szőllős, he'd hosted great hunts, with visitors—dignitaries, from time to time—joining him to hunt bustards, deer, rabbits, pheasants, and foxes. He showed the boys his guns, their intrigue matched only by his pride, and they stared wide-eyed and curious as he manipulated the weapon's mechanics.

One day, he'd even loaded blanks into the gun, shooting them inside the house as the boys shouted with delight. A loud knock on the door had come shortly after—the neighbors had sent the police to investigate.

Perhaps the most notable memory was when the family had marveled at Béla Bartók's growing fame. His image had been printed on the 1,000 Forint note—the new highest denomination in Hungarian money. Seeing Bartók's profile on the new green note seemed to trump all his previous accolades. Decades ago, his name was bestowed upon a main road that ran not far from the Zsombolyai apartment, and a towering Béla Bartók statue was erected in the park near the "bottomless pond" the boys loved so much.

A few years earlier, when Judit had brought the children for a visit, they'd toured a museum.

Halfway through the tour, a piano caught Obi's eye.

"That's ours," he said in that flat affect children often had.

"No, it's not," the curator laughed, looking to Judit for support. "It just looks like it!"

It was Bori who stepped in to defend the child's seemingly outlandish claim. "No, actually, it is, ma'am!" she said, her tone light and fun-loving. "We are Bartók's relatives, and the piano was in our family home for many years!"

Judit was proud of Béla's fame. Proud of her father's strength. Proud of her entire Hungarian family. Proud of her children. She was proud of Matthew, too.

He'd faced such difficult circumstances, and still emerged to build a career—and now a family business.

It was interesting to think about—her father had endured such strains over his life. The whole family had, really. Many of those difficulties shared a lot in common with the things Matthew had endured.

They had all survived—even thrived. Through revolutions and coups, through hunger and instability, so many of her loved ones had flourished.

The thought inspired her.

So much so, in fact, that on their return home, she determined to reach out to her friend Baerbel, a German and fellow member of Nigerwives. Judit had ascended in the organization, taking over as president of Nigerwives – Rivers State that year and the confidence she'd gained from the role motivated her to seek out more.

Baerbel had become the new headmistress of the Montessori school that Marika and Terike attended and, after the family's visit to Hungary—saturated in the family's musical accomplishments—she mustered the courage to ask if she could teach the little ones music.

"I have training in the Kodály method," she explained, her confidence increasing alongside her hope, "it's a way of teaching children—even very young children—the basics of music. We use things like clapping and other movements! They learn by feeling the music!"

Baerbel hadn't seemed to understand much of Judit's Kodály explanation, but it didn't matter—what mattered was that she said, "yes!"

Soon, Judit was teaching not only the nursery and primary school children at the Montessori school, but also the children at a second program, the Sacred Heart Seminary Secondary School.

She was bringing music education to the children of Rivers State! Like a dream come true, she stood before the children. Just as Mr. Berci and D^2P^2 had taught her all those years ago, just as she had once dreamed, before the reality of Communism had dashed her wishes to the ground.

Despite her efforts—despite, even, her pride at this opportunity—it seemed she couldn't win.

When she'd come home one afternoon after a day of teaching, Matthew had been waiting, irritated that he'd arrived home before her.

"You are a chemical engineer, not a music teacher," he'd said. She'd swallowed the hurt of his statement. Perhaps he was right.

After all, the wages were meager—little more than a pittance. As she progressed in her teaching, many of her lessons seemed to fall flat. The children weren't grasping the concepts, perhaps as a result of her broken English. Or perhaps, she thought with disappointment, it was because she wasn't cut out to be a teacher. She knew her communication skills weren't always the best, and she'd never had the opportunity to train as a teacher.

She refused to give up. Finally, she had an opportunity to feel like she was doing something worthwhile—she'd wanted that so badly! Now, her children could look at her as more than just a housewife—more than a weak, overly dependent woman, always corrected by her husband.

The children—particularly her older children—needed good role models now more than ever. As the boys grew older, it seemed they were less and less willing to follow her instructions without questioning or rebelling in one way or another.

Maybe teenagers were always just difficult to deal with.

Normal or not, it was frustrating—they would leave their things strewn around the floor or disregard her when she asked them to complete some long-deferred chore.

More than just frustrating, it was concerning. She wanted her children to succeed, as all mothers do. Her heart ached to see them making such poor choices.

Soon her worries would prove well-founded. When she came home from teaching one day, Ebinimi, Obi, and the house girl were beside themselves.

"What's wrong?" she asked them, dread rising in her voice.

"It's Tonye," her daughter gasped. "He is in big trouble!"

Chapter 21

WHITE HORSE

⎯⎯⎯

THERE HAD BEEN AN ACCIDENT.

The words alone made Matthew's heart leap into his throat. Every parent's nightmare, he returned home to find his wife frantic. Tonye and Obi had been in a three-car collision.

Tonye was in jail.

The boys had known where the family kept the Datsun Bluebird's keys. Left alone to their own teen devices, they'd taken the car for a joyride. They'd slammed into an oncoming Mercedes Benz and, in Tonye's attempt to steer away from the vehicle, crashed into a second Benz parked on the side of the road.

The damage to the three cars was extensive.

Tonye had been arrested, and Obi had fled the scene of the accident.

Both were physically safe.

At that news, the adrenaline of Mathew's worry transformed into a new, ugly rage. His mind flipped through all he wanted to say to the boys.

I told you not to drive the car!!

Do you know how dangerous the roads are?!

Do you know how much it costs to repair two Mercedes?!

The record played on repeat as he made his way through the jail to the cell and peered through the partition window at his cowering son among a crowded group of men wearing only underwear and sitting on the floor of the dark, dungeonous space. He walked him back out to the car for a tense, silent ride home. Even through his anger, he could feel the boy's fear.

He refused to comfort him—he refused even to break the silence with a stern word or a shout of exasperation.

He let Tonye feel the fear of what was coming. If it really sank in, maybe he would behave differently next time.

Because next time, they might not be so lucky.

So many of his fellow citizens had lost their lives on those roads, and he shuddered to think of how the outcome might have been different. He'd worried about the underdeveloped roads in Rivers State for as long as he could remember. Most of the state's towns and villages had no paved roads and still could only be accessed from the city by water. Despite Port Harcourt's six-hundred-thousand people—and growing—the city still had only one traffic light. Even skilled, attentive drivers lost their lives on these roads, let alone unsupervised teenagers.

He determined, then, that he would do two things.

First, he would flog them both every evening for a week. Tonye should have known better than to drive, and Obi shouldn't have left his brother alone at the scene.

Second, he would recommit to making positive changes in his community—not just the issue of traffic safety, but all of the other Riverine issues he'd been passionate about for years.

Ever since he was young, he'd immersed himself in the news, and he'd followed politics more than most. There were few people of Ijaw descent in government positions, and for months, people had been asking him if he would consider running.

The more he thought about it, the more he realized he could be an ideal candidate.

But how would he care for his family if he ran for office? As a public employee, he would have to quit his job to run. Leaving Waterglass Boatyard would be a big change for the family, especially in the face of a politician's uncertain financial future. While Matthew's salary was modest at best, it was reliable, and the company provided a car and other benefits. What would happen to JUMA?

But, as Judit had said, if good people abstained from politics, the country would never move in the right direction.

Matthew felt that sentiment deeply. As the country looked forward to transitioning from military rule to a civilian government, an air of optimism once again settled around him.

He wanted to be part of this new, exciting political world.

He needed to be part of it.

So, on June 3, 1989, he ran for the position of Rivers State Chairman of the People's Front of Nigeria, one of thirteen political parties in the country at the time. The campaign trail fit him like a glove, drawing on his natural charm and charisma. Being around like-minded people was exhilarating.

In the end, his budding political career—like all political careers—would come down to whether or not the people believed in him.

As it turned out, they did.

He plunged into his chairmanship, proudly displaying the green background and white stars of the People's Front flag. He took his role in the party very seriously, and he began his work of ensuring the People's Front stood strong against Nigeria's other parties.

The job was more important than ever.

However, only six months after he started as a party chairman, Nigerian politics were confronted with a jarring adjustment.

In December 1989, the country's Military President, General Ibrahim Babangida made a major announcement on reorganizing the Nigerian political party structure. The country's thirteen parties would be dissolved to establish two main parties wherein the previous parties had to realign—a system inspired by US politics.

This was an unexpected and frustrating blow to Matthew's budding political career. He knew that it came with obstacles, but he'd never imagined one quite of this stature. However, Matthew had never resisted a challenge. With his community and his family's stability on the line and the stakes of the upcoming election higher than ever before, he threw himself into the work.

Increased time away from home meant increased tension when he returned. Beyond being left alone with the children, Judit seemed to struggle with the idea of him holding such a position. With the consolidated parties and political campaigns ramping up rapidly, the stakes of his political venture were raised along with the responsibilities he was committing to.

He tried to ease her mind by involving her when he could— sometimes, this was even expected. At certain ceremonial activities, for instance, he would ask her to come along with him to be a supportive wife by his side.

Even those invitations seemed to fuel her insecurities.

In anticipation of one event, she brought home fabric to make herself new clothes.

"So you won't be so embarrassed of me," she said in Hungarian, the glint of her smile belied the concern behind her words.

"No, no, no, Jutka, that's not true," he said.

"But won't it seem strange to people?" she pressed. "That your wife is a foreigner?"

He tried his best to allay her fears, but he was drained by his heavy workload. He simply didn't have the energy to offer more than the most basic reassurances. Nor did he have much time to pause at all.

Determined to make his leadership an obvious choice for Nigeria's future, he campaigned for a position in one of the new political parties outlined by President Babangida.

"Aim high and shoot high," his father always said.

Now he was a father, repeating it to his sons.

He wanted his country to do the same—to set her sights on caring for her people and to follow through on the promise of reform.

No more coups.

The future of democratic rule was bright. And he would be part of the change.

He decided to join the Social Democratic Party—SDP for short. While he was new to this particular party, he brought with him his experience as Party Chair from his time with the People's Front.

He'd won a Chairmanship before. He could do it again.

After all, he felt called to make Nigeria better—to serve the Riverine people in the way he'd always wanted to see them served. That cause had no distinct political party—it was simply the right thing to do.

Given his natural proclivity to connect with others—to energize them and make them feel heard—this was his calling.

In a way, he was literally born to lead.

He'd heard plenty of stories about his father's determination—as a child, from as young as four years old, his father had been seen as mature for his age, responsible for home chores, and even marshaling his younger brothers when they were unruly. In part, this role was foisted on him after his mother died from complications in his own birth—with only one parent in the family, he'd had to step up from a very young age.

Matthew could see himself in his father's story, in a way. He'd been responsible as a child, too, setting ambitious future goals and contributing to his family where he could.

Matthew's grandfather had been even more like him—or, at least, Matthew imagined him that way. In truth, he'd never met his grandfather. The man had passed away long before he was born, but he had been well-known across the neighboring villages. A successful palm oil trader, he'd traveled across the rivers to adjoining towns and villages, collecting, processing, and selling his product. He was of the Ijaw tribe, a people who constituted the many towns and villages across the Niger Delta in southern Nigeria.

Just as his grandson would later be, his grandfather—Goldy, they called him, which was short for Golden—had been known for his cheerful personality and infectious laugh. Just like Matthew, most people he encountered loved him. Originally from Tombia, a small village situated along the River Nun, Goldy had relocated to his wife's home village of Nembe.

News of his death had saddened the Tombian people, who knew Goldy well from his travels—a successful trader, he often gave small gifts or a few schillings to his closest family members. Matthew could relate, having often given money to his relatives in the villages who always saw him as successful, regardless of his financial state.

Goldy's loss, Matthew had heard many times, was palpable.

Goldy's brother, Tasi Mamah, a short, stocky man with a strong-willed personality, was unhappy that Goldy had chosen somewhere else to start his family. He also felt his late brother's young wife incapable of caring for the children properly, and—as the now eldest son of the family—took action. Though their mother protested, he retrieved Matthew's uncles and father—only six years old at the time—to raise them in their father's homeland of Tombia. The three boys had adopted their uncle's first name, Tasi, as their surname.

When Matthew's father had been ordained a priest, he and his brothers had changed their names back to Mamah, to honor their late father and the home Tasi had ripped them away from. The name Mamah was not one that Nigerians generally recognized as Ijaw, and other than its obvious universal meaning, it did not translate to anything else in the language. The name was believed to be a synonym of the "Great Mother," Woyengi, historically the supreme deity of the Ijaw people. However, some speculated that its similarity to names from the Muslim North of the country suggests ancestral migration. Matthew's father had worn the name proudly in his priesthood travels, and his grandfather had ferried the name around his journeys as a palm oil trader.

In June of 1990, Matthew had once again been elected to a chairman position and bore the name into the villages he campaigned in for the Local Government Area (LGA) elections, this time under SDP's white horse logo.

Of course, this demanded travel. The work was overwhelming at times, but it was always rewarding. Even though he couldn't always be there for his family, he knew that his path could only help them—not only through his political income, but also by making Nigeria better for everyone.

As he campaigned around the region, he felt like a celebrity.

He and his entourage would crisscross Rivers State by speedboat, speaking with villagers about their concerns, gathering support, and spreading goodwill. At each new village, people flocked to them, their sharp, professional dress often a stark contrast to the shirtless and shoeless rural populations. The team wore formal, yet traditional attire, though they sometimes represented their campaign's logo on t-shirts and hats—a white horse on a field of green. Eventually, dozens, even hundreds, of people would surround them as they spoke.

It was strange to be on this side of things.

He recalled, as a boy, how he and his playmates would circle the village's visitors, trying to deduce who they were and what power they held. Back then, they'd pretended to be powerful leaders like the men who visited, mimicking their perceptions of the role's grandeur as they strutted around, waving and giggling.

He'd loved to imagine himself that way, as a well-respected man at the pinnacle of power.

When he looked back, it was hard to believe how much things had changed since he first moved to Port Harcourt, nervous, excited, and awestruck. He'd fantasized about his future path back then, but he couldn't imagine how it would feel—what it would mean to hold multiple degrees from prestigious international universities, to rise to the top of a public company, and, now, to travel the region campaigning for his party.

He'd had so much to learn back then.

As he watched his now teenage sons growing toward their own futures—futures he knew were bright, but could be irreversibly fragile—he wondered whether his father had held the same concerns about him.

The boys were undeniably talented.

Tonye was a skilled typist, rattling out seventy words per minute as he helped to type official documents. Sometimes he and his mother even went to the local university where he typed documents on a portable typewriter for extra spending money, an entrepreneurial instinct that would serve his son well.

Obi was a talented chess player. Both boys competed, representing Rivers State against other Nigerian youth. Sitting down to a match in the evenings offered Matthew true relaxation in the face of what could be a very stressful time.

He was grateful for them—for his entire family—especially as the pressure of the campaign rose to a fever pitch. As the party approached the local government election, SDP hoped to win control of as many localities as possible. The complicated political structure, comprised of fourteen local government areas and 192 wards, presented significant challenges under the new two-party system.

More time away from home, more stress, and more worries—as he fought hard for his party, he couldn't help but wonder whether his work was putting his family in danger. He cautioned Judit, urging her to make sure the children weren't out late. He didn't want Judit out late either, which posed a greater problem now that she was fully immersed in Nigerwives activities and meetings. As the election cycle wore on, he worried more and more about the family's safety.

Nevertheless, the energy of the campaign was electric—almost addictive. The enthusiasm of the crowd at every stop fed Matthew to his core. A chance to truly shine, he would speak in local colloquialisms, gaining the people's favor before ramping up the energy.

The campaign was usually stationed in a very rural village at a table and tent surrounded by lush greenery. However rudimentary their surroundings, Matthew and his team enlivened and energized the crowd with their ardor. Once the crowd was warmed up, he would begin his signature chant.

"SDP" he would shout, encouraging the people to chime in.

"PROGRESS!" the crowd responded.

"SDP!!"

"PROGRESS!!"

Once the crowds were on board, he would reverse the chant, calling on the crowd to complete his sentiment.

"PROGRESS?!"

Right on cue, the crowd roared.

"SDP!!"

Once the energy reached its peak—and not a moment later—he would quiet the crowd and launch into an address, always off the cuff, allowing him to adapt to the group's particular needs.

At one particular rally, he'd felt the intensity of the crowd's support. "Do you know the difference," he began, baiting the crowd, "between a horse and an eagle?"

The event's tension already high, he could almost feel his listeners leaning forward, puzzling over the answer. He drew out the pause with another breath before moving forward.

"The eagle," he continued, referencing his rival party's symbol, "is predatory...It captures and goes away!"

The crowd burst out in a mixture of cheers and jeering laughter.

The rousing speech demonstrated the loyalty and honor of the white horse, framing his own party as the hero and his opposition as villainous. Given the crowd's rousing response—the same response they got everywhere they went—he felt supremely confident about the SDP's chances of victory.

But when the results came back in March 1991, Rivers State LGA elections were split equally between the SDP and the NRC, the National Republican Convention. Later, after the results were contested by State officials, the case went to the tribunal, resulting in three NRC wards being overturned and awarded to the SDP. While the SDP had won the majority of chairmanships, the NRC still dominated the wards.

It was disappointing. Matthew had thought that SDP's campaign successes would result in a landslide victory. Instead, the results remained split nearly in half for Rivers State. Nevertheless, there was still work to be done. Primary elections for gubernatorial candidates would be held in August.

Matthew only grew more intensely focused on his political career.

Soon after the LGA elections in March, he received a discreet communication inviting him for a meeting with the SDP National Chairman, Baba Gana Kingibe.

The note made pride rise in Matthew's chest.

Chairman Kingibe wanted to speak with him directly. Perhaps, he realized, he shouldn't have been surprised. He'd been rising through the ranks of his party, demonstrating his skill as a politician and Chairman. Affirmations of his ability had mostly come from the enthusiastic crowds. Here, in this note, was confirmation that those at the top of the political hierarchy had noticed him, too.

Better yet, they believed in his potential.

Chapter 22

SKINS

J UDIT HAD NEVER IMAGINED HERSELF the
wife of a politician. With great pride, she recognized the
huge strides Matthew was making toward his dreams. He
was a born leader—she'd known it from the first time they met.
As he carved out his place in the Rivers State political arena, his
skills only grew more impressive.

But being the wife of a Nigerian politician had its drawbacks.

She'd often thought him somewhat overprotective. Years earlier,
when he'd first asked her to limit her driving—out of concern, she
knew—she'd tried to argue. So much of her days were taken up
with housework and children, cooped up in their little home. The
car offered freedom. A change of scenery.

But as Matthew's prominence rose, she saw the reasons behind
his concern. His campaigning took him away from home for long
stretches, and she was left with the children, vulnerable and nervous as her husband became known around the region.

Back in Europe, she'd occasionally taken medication to ease her
anxiety. These were unavailable in Port Harcourt, where mental

health services were limited to the city's single squalid psychiatric hospital. Nor did she have access to a psychotherapist. The only outlet she had was periodic discussions with her priest during confessions.

Struggling to feel stable and safe, she did what she could to hold everything together. She fasted and prayed, and for the past few years, had given up eating meat entirely. Her frustration—that acrid mixture of anxiety and irritation that resulted from her fear for the family's safety and the small annoyances of raising children—sometimes burst out of her, causing her to snap dramatically at her children.

In an attempt at reassurance, she reminded herself that little outbursts were nothing to worry about. She hated for neighbors to hear her yelling over some minor infraction—failing to pick up their room or leaving their things on the floor. That kind of frustration was expected from anyone busy with five children.

But her concerns about her marriage were more difficult to dismiss. When Matthew stayed out late at campaign events or arrived home in the early morning, hours after traveling across the region, she looked forward to seeing him. It seemed so rare that they had time to spend together.

That concerned her, too. They hadn't been intimate in some time, perhaps a normal consequence of their stress, but, she worried, perhaps also a sign of infidelity.

She shook off those thoughts and focused, instead, on greeting him when he came home. Late in the night, he'd creep quietly through the front door, careful not to wake the house, and she'd make him something to eat. She treasured that time together, grateful for the quiet of the house and the presence of her husband.

It wasn't easy—sometimes it seemed impossible—to strip off the uncertainty and fear, to trust that their future was secure.

But what else could she do?

Things needed to change, and the children would be ready for the next stages of their education soon. So, she and the children prepared to travel back to Hungary. Despite Matthew's urging that they tell no one about the trip—you could never be certain about people's intentions—she tried to focus not on Nigeria, but on the familiar comforts of Budapest.

She'd wanted to take the family to Hungary for some time. The boys were preparing to graduate secondary school, and Ebinimi was determined to take the final exam, too. They could explore postsecondary opportunities for the oldest children and ensure that Marika and Terike had a chance to immerse themselves in the Hungarian language.

Beyond education, she wanted the youngest children to build relationships with her family.

The thought sent a jolt through her chest.

While there was still time for the little girls to grow close to their grandmother, it pained her to think of returning to Hungary knowing that her father wouldn't be there.

He'd fallen ill several months earlier, with horrible pain in his legs that kept him in bed for most of the day. Hoping for the best, her mother had called the family doctor.

Shortly after, Judit had gotten word. If she wanted to see her father again before he passed, she needed to come home right away.

She traveled to Budapest that April, the airfare covered by Peter Bartók.

While her father had held on for another eight months, his health never returned. Judit had traveled alone back to Hungary for the funeral, to lay to rest this strong, brave man.

She felt grateful for his ninety years, for all the good he'd done as the family's patriarch, for the moments she'd watched him with the children, the moments he'd shown her what it meant to be both strong and tender.

And when they'd gotten the call with the news, she'd looked over to see Matthew crying.

She'd never seen it before.

But she understood.

Her father had taken Matthew in, as reticent as he had been early in their relationship, and he'd nurtured and cared for them as they built a family. The two men had grown close—the two men she loved most.

As the family packed to return to Hungary, her two teenage sons, a teenage daughter, and two growing girls, she realized there were two other men in her life now—Obi and Tonye were seventeen years old, and, although they would always be her babies, they saw themselves as men, ready to take on the world.

Ebinimi felt ready to leave the nest, too. Determined to take the secondary school certificate exam at only fifteen, her daughter refused to hear arguments that she was too young. Ebinimi was strong-willed and a skilled student. Judit knew her daughter would soon leave, too.

All three of her oldest children, gone. Off to discover what their lives had to offer.

It was hard to do that in Nigeria. There, teacher strikes sometimes caused schools to close for days or weeks—even months. Her children would need better access if they were to truly live up to their potential—and they had the potential to be truly great.

So the six of them—Judit and the children—traveled to Hungary. She'd expected the apartment to feel cold and empty without the warm presence of her father. As her mother welcomed them in, she knew she'd been wrong. Things were much as they had been before.

A large, wooden, 1970s black and white television stood in the living room, functioning more effectively as decor than a working set. Bookcases flanked the console, adorned with floral patterns her father had painted a long time ago. An assortment of vases and trinkets lay around the shelves. Ceramic fireplaces still stood in each room, sometimes used for heating with the help of the firewood they stored in the communal basement.

But while the warmth of the family home felt like a constant around them, Hungary had changed.

Two years earlier, Communism had come to a surprisingly peaceful end. It was the future so many had dreamed of back in 1956, when Judit had gazed out of the apartment window at the optimism below—a free, democratic parliamentary election that resulted in the ascent of József Antall, a former teacher and librarian, as Prime Minister.

Just months later, the last of the Soviet troops left Hungary.

And yet, the Soviets' exit hadn't resulted in the utopia so many had anticipated. The Russians had held their thumb over the people of Hungary for so long. For most, that had been an injustice.

Judit's own life trajectory had been changed forever—a fact she was now glad for. After all, her career in engineering brought her Matthew and their beautiful family.

If she'd grown up without Soviet restriction, she realized, her options would have been unlimited. The thought was bittersweet for her but exciting for the children, who would benefit from everything she'd missed. They could even go to seminary, as her

brother hoped, although neither she nor the boys had much interest in that direction.

The country had finally found freedom!

But freedom, they soon learned, carried consequences.

Groups of young neo-Nazi skinheads ran rampant in the
streets, unmistakable with their shaved heads and black or olive
satin jackets. Scowling at anyone who looked foreign, they stared,
sometimes even jeered, when Judit walked by with the children.
Their menacing presence made her skin crawl with the feeling of
being watched, the skinheads' choice to refrain from violence only
reminded her of the possibility of attack.

It reminded Judit of the family's stories about World War II.
Those same dark thoughts must have weighed heavy on her father's
mind in February 1945, when several loud knocks landed on the
Koós apartment door.

"*Chasy*! *Chasy*!!" the Russian soldiers had shouted. Compared to
the threatening semi-automatic rifles in their hands, their words
seemed almost reasonable. Judit's mother described how the
thumping of her heartbeat had drowned out the soldier's voices
as they made their way around the apartment, apparently pleased
with the terror they caused.

"Chasy!" the soldier yelled again, indicating his watch pocket.

At that, her father had drawn out his watch as her mother raced
to collect other valuables, handing them over in hopes that the
soldiers would leave.

And they did. For a time, at least.

These kinds of things had a way of lingering in the air, dark
and thick where the intruders' feet had stepped, their invisible
fingerprints like a spectral calling card reminding them that the
danger could return at any moment.

It must have been horrible for her parents to feel so powerless in their own home.

Like outsiders, even in the one place they are supposed to belong.

She'd felt the contradiction deeply on her return to Hungary, as she saw the skinheads narrowing their eyes at her children, as friends warned them about the risk of being out alone at night. Darker skinned than the average Hungarian, her children were obvious targets. Tonye and Obi hadn't been particularly concerned, sometimes even laughing at the possibility.

They'd never experienced racism, so they couldn't imagine being hated by someone who didn't even know them.

But Judit could. If she'd learned one thing from Nigerian politics—not to mention her own parents' experiences—it was that, while most people were good, some were very, very bad. She'd felt it acutely in Nigeria as Matthew's political involvement increased, and now she felt it here, in her home city, as these horrible young people snarled at her beautiful children.

She knew terrible things could happen—they happened to people every day.

And then she saw Tonye's face.

Bloody and bruised, the dark shadows spreading under his eyes, her son looked strangely calm, standing there in the entryway of the apartment, his black coat smeared with blood and his nose plugged with gauze.

Her stomach flipped and a gasp caught in her throat. Heart thumping behind her ears and bile rising in her throat, she went to him—calm, he needed her to stay calm.

"Oh, Tonye," she said. Her fingers instinctively went to the seventeen-year-old's nose, but she stopped herself, her hand hovering over his swollen face. When she looked at him, she only saw the little boy he'd been, smart and strong, but too brave. Determined to grow up too fast.

"It's okay, Anyu," he replied, somehow reassuring her despite his poor, beaten face. "I'm alright."

She'd tried to protect him, tried to warn him, and, when she felt most helpless, tried to tell herself that her worrying was silly—just more anxiety over nothing. But she'd feared this night since she saw that first pack of olive-green jackets.

Now her fears had come true.

Helping him remove the bloody coat, she asked what had happened.

"I saw them when I was getting on the subway," he recounted. "I sat down like I always do."

He'd been working at Reflex Kft, an animation studio, painting hand-drawn celluloid sheets for foreign animated films. The job seemed so exciting, and she'd long tried to convince him to use his artistic talent to carve out a career, urging him to consider architecture. He resisted, calling art a hobby, despite his enjoyment and interest in his current project: the American film, *A Troll in Central Park*.

But to get between work and the Zsombolyai apartment, he'd had to take the subway.

That night, six skinheads had spotted him, boarding the train after him.

"As soon as the car started moving…it happened very fast. One of the skinheads walked in front of me and suddenly stomped on my face. The others then joined in…"

They'd hit him until they exited at the next stop, breaking his nose in two places. He'd been focused on protecting his eyes and teeth which, mercifully, were uninjured.

As he recovered over the next few days, relatives stopped by, several of them angry enough to consider revenge. Her older cousins, in particular, had threatened to bait the skinheads, finding a way to hurt them the way they'd hurt Tonye.

But he wouldn't hear of it.

Oddly, he was jovial and not depressed as the family expected.

But Judit didn't feel jovial at all. It was hard to say what she felt. Realizing right away that Tonye wouldn't want her to panic, she held back her strongest reactions. But the incident shifted something in her heart.

She'd realized, of course, how evil people could be to one another. The family's stories from the war showed that much.

But she'd never thought she would have to protect her own children from such violence.

In her home country, no less.

She prepared a cold compress—the doctors had told Tonye it would help with the swelling. Once he was settled in, she retreated to her bedroom and prayed the rosary.

The next morning, she marched down to the church. So many things were out of her control, but her faith never failed her.

She convinced the priest to allow her to organize Catholic masses dedicated to ending racial persecution in three churches: the Franciscan church at Ferenciek tere, the Rock Chapel by Gellért Hill, and the small chapel on Ulászló Street, which the family frequented, led by Father Dr. István Kovács. Racial injustice was mentioned in the sermons and tolerance was promoted.

It seemed like such a small thing, but it comforted her. She'd taken a stand against something horrible, trying, as Matthew was doing in Nigeria, to make the world a better place.

In spite of it all, life went on.

Tonye resigned from the animation studio, despite his supervisors' best attempts—they'd even come to the house, hoping to convince him to stay.

Ebinimi found a well-paying job at Staff-to-Go, a secretarial temp service. Because she spoke English—as all of the children did—she was seen as a particularly desirable employee.

Her brothers started work there soon after, and, throwing her hat in the ring, too, Judit joined them at the company. She wasn't as good at the typing part of the job—for that, she leaned on Tonye's skill—but it gave her something to do and allowed her to be close to her children.

She didn't have much longer with them, after all.

Getting the boys into universities was more difficult than Judit had hoped. Despite their strong potential, the family struggled to find enough money to cover tuition costs. Peter Bartók agreed to cover Tonye's education if he were to get into medical school. Grateful for Peter's help, he studied desperately for the entrance examination and was ecstatic when he was admitted to Semmelweis Medical School in Budapest. Obi would apply the following year.

And Ebinimi, to Judit's pride, passed the secondary exam thanks to her incredible dedication to her studies. At only sixteen years old, she applied to colleges in the US, gaining acceptance at Barton County Community College, in a place called Kansas.

Back home, Judit assumed, politics were still progressing as they had been, with Matthew persistently aiming high and shooting high.

He'd taught their children well, she realized, as she thought about their ambitious future plans. They both had. Although perhaps she shouldn't think of them as "children" anymore, now that they'd risen through their schooling and were set to enter the world as adults.

It made her even more grateful to hold her two little ones close. As she walked Marika and Terike home from school one afternoon—from Bocskai Elementary, where the older children had attended years before—her heart soared.

"The teacher says 'mahn-kee,' Anyu!" Marika exclaimed, commenting on the teacher's accent. "Instead of 'monkey'!"

Terike erupted into a fit of giggles at that, and, encouraged by her sister's reaction, Marika pressed on. "And 'vahn' when she means 'one'!"

The girls' laughter was contagious, and, though she tried to remind the girls to be kind, she found herself drawn into their silliness.

Life would be different without the older children. With her father gone. Away from Matthew until they returned to Nigeria.

But she could get used to it—at least for a little while. She could slow down and embrace these little moments of joy.

That really was what life was all about.

Chapter 23

FLAG BEARER

"SDP!"

"PROGRESS!!!"

"SDP!"

"PROGRESS!!!"

"PROGRESS?!" Matthew shouted in question, firing up the crowd.

"S-D-P!!!" they roared in answer.

Masses of white-and-green-clad supporters surrounded Matthew on all sides, growing louder with each repetition of the signature call-and-response chant. Just like he had at every campaign stop along the way—just as he would continue to do as they crisscrossed the Riverine region recruiting SDP supporters—Matthew turned his body from side to side, drawing in the crowd by signaling to them when it was their turn to shout their response.

In a way, the pattern had become routine.

But nothing felt routine in the city's largest soccer stadium, surrounded by thousands of people. His party, driven by his hard work and community-building efforts, had drawn this mass of supporters to a huge, energizing rally. As he turned the proverbial podium over to the group of traditional dancers—meant to warm up the crowd with entertainment before he launched into a speech on the importance of voting—his sparkling smile was genuine. The event would culminate with a soccer match between women and older men from SDP to promote light spirits and engagement with SDP's messages.

Politics was a cutthroat, dangerous game, but with his people's access to resources on the line, it was a challenge worth accepting.

He motioned for the dancers to take the field, their brightly colored costumes standing in bold contrast to his own clothing. When they visited the villages, trudging up the jetty as children circled eagerly around them, they sometimes wore casual clothing—party-branded t-shirts and baseball caps with an image of a horse rearing back, the SDP's logo. It was borrowed, as was the NRC's eagle, from the Nigerian coat of arms. His clothing for the stadium that day was in a similar fashion, just a white t-shirt and simple pants.

Other events, like visiting with village chiefs to pay respects and ask for community buy-in, demanded more formal clothing. He and the other SDP officials typically donned tunics that fell just short of the knee over lightweight pants, a more traditional look that signaled their trustworthiness and determination to serve the people of Rivers State.

By then, they were laser-focused on the gubernatorial race, to be held in August 1991. After years of political disruption caused by coups, corruption, and a general distrust of the shifting political climate, they realized they needed to educate their supporters as much as rally them. People needed to know how to vote, where to vote, and when to vote. They needed to understand the urgency of this election as a chance to shore up a strong, bold democratic government.

They needed to understand that the party was seeking candidates—the brightest and the best among their supporters needed to spur into action.

The party had a few names on their list already, of course, of people who had participated in the government before, but they hoped for some newcomers, too.

So Matthew went on the radio to announce that SDP was accepting nominations for gubernatorial candidates, explaining the ins and outs of registering and, hopefully, charming a few new faces to step forward.

In the end, fourteen potential candidates signed up.

The list included some names Matthew knew, as well as a few he hadn't heard before. As Matthew scanned the names, two stood out: Samson Amadi and E. D. Beregha.

Sporting a dark complexion and prominent brow, Amadi communicated a solemn dedication to many of the same issues Matthew supported—infrastructure and education, most notably. An accountant and businessman, he was popular among the crowds, particularly among his fellow Ikwerre indigenes.

Beregha was known for his fedoras and cold, stoic expressions, both of which radiated a sense of cutthroat politics—a determination to play for keeps and win at all costs. Even so, his behavior on the campaign trail had been surprisingly over the top, at least as far as Matthew was concerned.

For one thing, Beregha had filed a serious complaint against Matthew, stating that he had unfairly favored Amadi on the campaign trail. The accusation was quickly dispelled through a letter to the election commission.

But as they approached the primaries, Beregha continued to spread mayhem. He made an unveiled threat against the Rivers State SDP, the portion of the party Matthew was responsible for leading.

"If I don't win the upcoming primaries," the man wrote, "we both know why. If that happens, I'll bring the SDP to its knees."

Matthew had been surprised at his forwardness but hoped it was overstated. Surely Beregha's threats were mostly puffed-up displays of strength. After all, even if the man tried to bring the party down, he didn't have the power to do so. The SDP could withstand a little bullying.

Matthew truly believed that.

Until Beregha's men showed up.

Matthew was seated in his office when he heard shouting near the front of the SDP secretariat. Fearing the worst, he peered through the door. A stream of men was entering the building. Near the front entrance, one man was tearing posters and announcements from the bulletin board. Another snatched papers from behind the reception desk, mangling the pages as he did. As they paraded through the door, Matthew thought he counted at least twenty-five men—perhaps even thirty.

"Go and call police," he barked into the phone. "Quick, quick!"

Fortunately, the officers arrived quickly before the men could do significant damage.

When it was revealed that Beregha had sent the men as "thugs" to wreak havoc on the secretariat, Matthew feared the implications for the coming election cycle.

Now that Beregha had threatened his office, he had no reason to doubt the man's promise to destroy the Rivers State SDP.

He wasn't sure of the best path forward. On one hand, this type of violence could not stand—having received death threats already, he knew where such actions would lead. But, on the other, perhaps it wouldn't serve the party well to push back against Beregha, a strong candidate in his own right—and one who had already accused Matthew of siding too openly with Amadi.

In the end, Matthew requested that several areas, including Okrika, Elele, Brass, Isiokpo, and Port Harcourt be put under surveillance for the primaries. That provided some reassurances at least—even though police were unreliable, some supervision would surely discourage any escalations.

Still, the incident sat like a rock in his gut as the SDP moved forward to their gubernatorial primary election.

He had been right to worry.

Fourteen candidates ran for the SDP primaries on October 19, 1991. Complaints of alleged irregularities were lodged. In Okrika, no other candidate's picture was allowed to be displayed except that of the local candidate Beregha. There were also threats and vandalism there by SDP members led by the local party chairman. Any voter who stood behind the picture of a candidate other than Beregha was threatened or beaten. Outsiders were moved into the wards to improve voting counts or enter fake data.

An increasing level of vitriol was directed at Matthew.

Literally threatened with death if he announced the primary results, Matthew had already written to the Commissioner of Police requesting twenty-four-hour armed guards for a one-week protection at the SDP secretariat as well as his home. His physique had rounded slightly from stress and travel.

He valued his safety, but he also valued political progress.

So, despite the threats of violence and fraud, Matthew refused to back down. He carried on with the election as though everything was as it should be. When he scoured the election results, the votes tabulated on a large sheet of paper created by taping together several standard-sized pages, he wasn't sure how to feel.

Samson Amadi—the candidate Matthew had been accused of favoring—had received forty percent of the approximately seven-hundred-thousand votes.

Amadi had won the honor of running as SDP's gubernatorial flagbearer.

Beregha had placed second.

While he knew the situation could lead to backlash and instability, he had no time or energy to be concerned about the failed candidate's reaction. The man would reap the rewards of his deplorable behavior. For now, there were more important things to worry about.

Matthew remained as determined as ever to run an honest, straightforward campaign. No matter what happened, he would not allow himself to be pulled into the corruption that lurked like a viper, lying in wait with an eye toward attack.

He could easily have gotten involved in the scandals. While some believed he lived a lavish life, his salary had decreased steadily over the years, sinking to less than he'd previously made at Waterglass Boatyard—an all-time low.

And yet, he could not be swayed toward corruption. The Rivers State people had real needs—needs that went far beyond his own. Needs that could not be satisfied without real, authentic political change.

His father's recent illness was a staunch reminder. Having fallen quite ill, he'd been in bed for two weeks with no access to medical care. Matthew immediately sent money, despite having little to give, and arranged for a boat to bring his father to Port Harcourt.

He looked terrible. Lying motionless in the clinic, eyes glassy and jaw slack, he looked near death, and Matthew once again vowed to fight for village infrastructure that might have prevented his prognosis from growing so poor. The family physician, Dr. Didia, determined that the older man's blood pressure was quite high and, with a shake of the head, told Matthew that his father was in the early stages of cardiac failure.

Matthew had always known that the people of the riverine villages lacked access to things many urban Nigerians took for granted—clean water and food, paved roads, medical care—because his family frequently visited Port Harcourt. They would show up at his door asking for money, not only to support themselves, but to pay for their trip back to the village.

It didn't have to be this way.

Having traveled around the world, Matthew knew that other countries provided at least a basic semblance of care, even for those in the most remote, rural areas.

Perhaps these things could be possible with an SDP-backed governor. Perhaps Amadi could deliver on the promises Matthew had dreamt of since childhood. Even if Amadi was an upland Ikwerre and not of riverine extraction. It would only require some strategic campaigning—the right messaging—to help people see that things could be different. Better.

But they didn't see it—at least not at first.

Shortly after Amadi's win was announced, protests broke out across the region. All thirteen losing candidates came together to publicly release a statement claiming massive fraud. Amadi, Matthew, and the state electoral officer now faced accusations of intimidation and assault.

Similar protests succeeded in demanding a redo of the primary elections for forty-eight State House of Assembly seats, nineteen

LGA chairmanship seats, and 271 councillorship seats. To add to the confusion, the federal government also carved out entirely new LGAs from the existing fourteen.

As challenging as the situation was, Matthew still embraced it. He felt confident in his party even then—believing without a doubt that SDP could move Rivers State in the right direction.

He went along with a redo of the Rivers State LGA election— not that he had much choice—trusting that the outcome could only help the SDP.

Amid all the ridiculous claims of fraud and election tampering, he was vindicated! In fact, the results were even clearer than the first time, with a larger portion of the vote going to SDP, nearly across the board—SDP won ten out of nineteen LGA chairmanships and 123 councillorships, a striking victory compared to the NRC's 108.

He'd done well leading the party, even in his early days in the role. And this proved it.

He all but strutted into the secretariat for the next few days, chin up, chest out, and thoughts laser-focused on the full gubernatorial election.

"Operation Takeover '91" was in full swing.

They marked the occasion with an address. Speaking to the SDP Rivers State Congress in mid-November, Matthew officially ratified Samson Amadi as SDP's gubernatorial candidate, giving way to what would be an intense two-day campaign with a tour scheduled through the state.

It felt electric. As long as he could remember, he'd practiced aiming high and shooting high. He'd never thought he would be here—pushing his entire state to aim even higher, to shoot even higher, and to use the full hand of the government to achieve their dreams.

He should have known how cruel the thrill of victory could be for Nigerian politicians. One day, a person could be at the very top of their influence, beloved by the people, and effective in their role.

And the next, it could all be gone.

He'd allowed himself to forget, but the National Electoral Commission soon reminded him.

"The SDP primary election has been canceled," their note read. "A new election must be conducted."

Snatching a sheet of paper from the office drawer, he feverishly typed his objection. There was no proof of massive rigging, falsification of figures, or any of the other malpractices alleged against Amadi. The cancelation was outrageous.

Despite his strongly worded objection, the committee held firm. A new Rivers State gubernatorial primary would have to be conducted. Amadi would not be allowed to run.

They would have just nine days to make arrangements!

Providing some small comfort was the fact that, at the very least, the NRC's candidate had been disqualified, too, after urging by SDP that their competing party be held to the same standards.

There was another bright spot, too.

As the party began to reorganize, strategizing for this unfortunate—and, in their opinion, highly unfair—new election, one of Matthew's party leaders pulled him aside.

"Doc," he said. "This is a sign. You should have been the one running all along."

Raising his eyebrows, Matthew shot the man a smug look. "Eh?" he replied, folding his arms across his chest.

"Of course!" the man urged. "You're more qualified than anybody on the list! Who else has a doctorate? Who else has worked in public and private sectors?"

He'd realized this, too, even looking over the incoming screening questionnaires as the month rolled to a close.

The man pressed on, insistent. "What would stop you from running?"

To that, Matthew had no answer.

He shook his head. "What are you talking about?" he laughed, disarming the man's intensity.

The man met his teasing comment with a serious stare. "Think about it."

So Matthew did.

When he thought of all he could do with a governorship, he could hardly hold himself back. He could provide potable drinking water, improve transportation and education, provide boreholes, increase road construction, fund educational scholarships, and ensure textbooks and adequate wages for teachers.

He knew all of these priorities would resonate with his people—he'd spoken with them many times in his travels around the state.

He'd had no answer when the man had asked, *what would stop you from running?*

Before Matthew knew it, he was holding a poster in his hand that showed his picture, confident with close-cropped hair.

Above his picture, it read, "Rivers State VOTE." At the bottom of the poster, in big, bold, black letters, the call to action continued, "Dr. Matthew O. Mamah for Governor."

As a nod to his most consistent platform—anticorruption in the Nigerian government—his slogan read, "a symbol of unity, justice, and fairness."

It felt good to look at the poster—a physical manifestation of his father's "aim high, shoot high" urgings. But the poster was flimsy, too, and not just in its paper form. Something about it seemed unbelievable, like the translucent dreams that came during the early morning hours.

Something had shifted in Amadi when the commission disqualified him. Once an ardent supporter of the SDP, he turned almost imperceptibly sour. It weighed heavy on Matthew's mind.

How would Amadi react to his closest colleague taking his place?

Matthew wasn't sure.

That alone wouldn't stop him from running—although, of course, he didn't want to be seen as stabbing Amadi in the back.

He'd also felt certain that running another Ikwerre indigene in the SDP position would excite Amadi, helping the man shift gracefully from candidate to backer and encouraging his supporters to back his tribesman. The Ikwerres had been some of the party's biggest supporters, rallying behind Amadi just as Matthew had. If Matthew continued his candidacy, the tribe would be upset that another Ikwerre hadn't been selected to run.

As party chair, Matthew had a responsibility to serve. Perhaps his service was most beneficial in keeping the party on an even keel. The best way to ensure a smooth transition into the new elections—to maintain the loyalty of SDP supporters and promote peace and order—was to find the ideal candidate.

So Matthew reconsidered his candidacy and began to search for a candidate he knew everyone would support.

The new candidate soon emerged in Chief Eric Aso, a stocky man with a round face he always framed with sunglasses. This man could maintain the party's momentum as they pushed through the repeated primary and plunged ahead into the main race for governor.

Matthew was certain of it.

Until the rumors began.

The campaign season was short—barely enough to be called a "season" once the redo election was factored in. Even in the short days they had to campaign, gossip circulated that Amadi was turning his supporters against Aso, discouraging their support of SDP.

When the dust settled, Aso had won nearly two-thirds of the gubernatorial primary vote. The primary did little to further the region's infrastructure and opportunities. To do that, they needed to win the election.

That goal seemed less and less achievable.

Matthew never gave up. It wasn't in his nature. So, continuing to rally—with bright, welcoming smiles and bold chants—he kept up his energy and that of the party. Maybe they could actually pull this thing off. He felt the fatigue in his bones, but he could push through for these final days before the election.

In 1991, Rivers State voters made their choice between Aso and the NRC's Chief Rufus Ada George.

Matthew took note as the votes came in, tallied on large charts in the SDP office. But as the day wore on, he became more and more pessimistic.

In the end, all of Matthew's work—his blood, sweat, and tears—was for nothing.

Chief Ada George won.

Unsurprisingly, election irregularities were claimed, with reports of higher-than-expected ballots cast and results from at least three regions where elections did not take place.

It didn't matter.

SDP lost.

He lost.

Chapter 24

THREE FATHERS

———

"**D**ADDY, ARE YOU NO MORE in SDP?" Marika demanded.

After a long flight from Hungary, the girls were surprised to find the house scrubbed of SDP paraphernalia. They'd last seen every surface littered with hats and t-shirts and stickers emblazoned with the green and white horse logo. It all seemed to have vanished, as if only a dream. Even the gray SDP car—which was occasionally used to transport the family—was missing from the front of the house. In its place, there were NRC materials sprinkled about.

Following her daughter's lead, Judit placed her suitcase on the floor as she slid her purse from her shoulder.

"Apu?" the little girl pressed.

"No, no..." he hesitated, eagerly grabbing two of their suitcases and retreating into the bedroom.

The girls looked up at their mother with curiosity. Judit knew, at least from what Matthew said over the phone, that the fallout from the election had forced her husband to switch parties, but she merely shrugged and sent the girls to their room.

They'd fought about rooms during the flight, both of them hoping to take over the only room with an air conditioner—their sister's room.

The thought of Ebinimi's room standing empty made Judit's heart clench. How could her eldest daughter have grown up so quickly and moved away to America at only sixteen years old? She knew Ebinimi was ready to spread her wings, but she felt a pang in her chest, her pride in her strong, independent daughter mixed with grief for losing her daily presence.

It seemed like just yesterday that Ebinimi had toddled after her older brothers, insisting on her right to be treated as an equal despite the fact that she was, at the time, the youngest. Seemingly overnight, she'd grown into a striking young woman who was more than capable of taking care of herself.

Judit had wound up with five strong-willed children, and, somehow, she'd kept up with them. Their stubborn self-assurance meant they needed extra guidance. Perhaps that was why her career had gone in the direction it had—perhaps she was always meant to be home, taking care of her children. Certainly, she couldn't have had the same effect on their personalities if she had been distracted by a career.

They'd been molded well, she thought, as she sent the three oldest off into adulthood. God would watch over them—she prayed, daily, that it would be so. She trusted that He would guide their judgment just as she had tried to during their childhood.

As for her two youngest, much work remained.

Ten years old now—twice the age Tonye and Obi were for their first Holy Communion—and the girls still hadn't officially taken the sacrament.

It wasn't for her lack of trying.

She'd twice enrolled them in catechist groups at the St. John's Church in Port Harcourt. With each attempt, Judit was appalled at the approach. The Bible had so much to offer children—tales of comfort and adventure, stories of brave children not much older than they were, and, of course, cautionary tales about those who strayed. But for children, these stories were best told with an animated expression or interactive play. At least, that's how she would have taught the lessons.

Instead, her girls would return home from their sessions with dull, bored faces.

"What did you learn?" she'd ask.

"To be good," they'd answer, after a brief pause.

The first time, she'd thought it was just a fluke. Perhaps their teacher was just unusually strict. Or maybe they just hadn't gotten to the exciting parts yet.

But then she'd overheard part of a class where the teacher explained the Holy Trinity. Even to her ears—an adult woman who'd been fascinated by religion her entire life—the explanation was opaque and overly sophisticated.

Worse than that, when one of the children couldn't repeat the explanation back to the teacher, the teacher had balled her hand into a fist, and with the jutted-out knuckle of her middle finger, conked him on the head!

Shortly thereafter, the children had been given a test. Marika had failed. When Judit asked the teacher why, she was told that her daughter hadn't known the rosary.

This was absolute rubbish, of course. Both girls could recite the rosary easily, without a single stumble, but apparently, the church was more concerned about proper definitions and pronunciations than about the concept of prayer. Her daughter hadn't known the word "annunciation," and, despite understanding the meaning of the rosary, the girls had been forced to begin classes again.

Again, their Communion was delayed. The priest even made a ridiculous demand that they wait three more years so they could "gain enough maturity for the sacrament."

It was beyond frustrating. She'd found such comfort in religion growing up. The church had guided her to become the woman she was—a generous mother, an attentive wife, and someone who helped those she loved grow closer to God.

Church was absolutely foundational for children to grow into happy, healthy adults.

During their stay in Hungary, when the boys were younger, the task had been so much easier. The family priest, Father István, or Pisti Bácsi as the children called him, had been a pediatrician before taking his vows. Always encouraging the children, he'd been an excellent teacher.

She'd had to fight to get them their first Communion before the family moved to Nigeria—they were only five years old, and most of the children in the catechism classes were six, but since they planned to leave the country, the church had made an exception.

With Marika and Terike, she lacked the kind of support she'd had with the older children. It wasn't just the issue of overly stern teaching methods. Even adult-focused church activities were disorganized in Port Harcourt, so it was no wonder the catechism classes lacked the special touches she'd come to expect in Europe.

Still, this was one battle she would not lose.

So, with some reluctance, she joined a Catholic Women's Organization. While she hoped to make a positive change to the cultural issues she saw all around her, her focus had to be on ensuring that Marika and Terike had solid foundations in the church.

They needed to learn the power of prayer—not just for themselves, but because the family needed it now more than ever. Matthew had returned from a trip to Budapest with anxious news. While most of the family was doing well, Uncle Béla had fallen ill. He had few details, other than to say that the older man—her second father—was not well enough to have guests.

Helpless and distraught, she did the only thing she could think of—she gathered the family together to pray, just as she had done as a child. She feared the worst for him, but she also felt the power of the family's shared prayers bringing them together. As they prayed together—night after night—she thought she could sense the girls growing closer to God.

It drove her to keep pushing. Focusing on the things she could do to support childhood religious education, she began working with the women's organization to put together a small children's program, allowing the kids to apply the things they learned in catechism to fun activities like coloring or planting flowers.

To her delight, the girls picked up on the messages quickly.

Finally, they finished the classes—the relief she felt was enormous—and took their first Holy Communion.

She wrote to Uncle Béla and Aunt Judit to share the good news and to wish them well.

Despite all her hopes and their prayers, when the phone rang, she knew the news couldn't be good.

"Judit, Uncle Béla has passed," her mother said. The breath drained from her lungs and time seemed to stop for a moment as she lowered herself into a dining room chair.

Uncle Béla was gone.

Before she could answer, her face was wet with tears. She'd known he was ill. She'd known he was old. That knowledge did little to prepare her for the overwhelming grief.

Uncle Béla had been her rock. He'd been the one to convince her father to accept Matthew. He'd nurtured and cared for her. Introduced her to a home full of shiny vases packed with flowers and clocks and walls lined with encyclopedias.

"Jutka?"

"Yes," she said, "I'm here. I'm—" She paused, wondering what she should say. No words seemed to capture the distance between her and her family. "I'm so sorry to hear that."

They'd ended the call quickly—international rates were enormously expensive. As soon as she heard the phone click into its cradle, she leaned her head in her hands and wept.

Time moved so quickly.

The only comfort she took was that Uncle Béla, along with her father, could now watch over her in ways others couldn't. From Heaven, they now knew all of her inner feelings.

She watched the children with Matthew, home much more often now that the election season had ended. When his father came to stay with them in July—Papa, they called him—she saw how the care of older generations could foster the kind of morality she wanted for Marika and Terike.

He would help put the girls to bed, saying the rosary with them despite his denominational difference, and even kneeling despite the creak of his knees and the persistent aches he felt.

Not long before, he'd fallen so sick that doctors thought he wouldn't make it. After Matthew had paid to bring him to Port Harcourt, they both knew the older man was too weak to return to the village.

She'd been nervous, at first, to have such a sick man at their home—not for fear of contagion or burden, but because she worried that she wouldn't know what to do if he needed emergency care.

She soon settled into the routine of having him around. He was so curious, asking her endless questions about Hungary and sharing his perspective on her struggles with the girls' Catholic education. An Anglican priest, he might have rejected her perspective on religion, but he never had a bad word to say.

Once, he'd asked her directly why Catholics prayed to Mary. She'd told him that Jesus had expected it, equating Christ's love of his mother to the older man's fondness for his own mother, despite the fact that she'd died when he was an infant.

Instead of arguing back, he had sat, thoughtful for a moment, before nodding in sincere understanding.

He was so gentle. Kind.

She knew from Matthew's stories that he hadn't always been, but as a grandfather, he showed his genuine care with every breath.

It made her heart soar.

Though he wasn't well enough to travel back to the village, Matthew's father had recently traveled to visit his estranged wife—a gesture of his lingering care toward the mother of his children as his health had begun to fade.

As Judit watched him over the months, they spent hours speaking about their different cultures, religious viewpoints, and life in general. She grew to love him like her own father.

A third father, perhaps, now that the other two were gone.

Death was a terrible thing.

Sometimes she thought of her mother and Aunt Judit, widowed after such long, happy marriages, and her eyes would well with tears. She thought of her own marriage in those moments, wondering whether she could survive without Matthew. She might not even survive the trauma of losing him.

Perhaps she wouldn't want to.

As macabre as the thought was, she realized she hoped that they would die together. The pain of being left behind was simply too great—much greater, surely, than leaving this earth behind.

As she and Papa grew closer over the months he stayed with them, she refused to feel sad or even resigned.

She had been given an opportunity to show love and to see love—a chance to raise her girls with a caring, grandfatherly presence. She meant to cherish it as long as she could.

Because she knew that they didn't have much time left.

And late one night in December, Papa, her third father, slumped suddenly in his bed. Matthew had been away with their only car, so Judit ran to their neighbor, Mrs. Okonny. She drove them to the Braithwaite Memorial Hospital, Judit massaging Papa's head and chest as they traveled. She feared how she would handle his death alone, and how Matthew would feel about his absence from the event.

Their efforts, and those of hospital staff, could not stop the death of a sick, elderly man.

Two of her fathers had left her.

Too soon after, Papa left, too.

She was grateful that Papa didn't die in her arms or without Matthew present. She thanked God for that.

That mercy did little to ease the real pain, the emptiness that filled her chest, the unnatural stillness of the home, and the sense of someone missing.

The choking feeling of abandonment.

It truly was the cruelest part of death—the way life kept going, withholding even the smallest space of comfort and rest for the survivors of the dead.

Papa was gone. But Judit still had two young girls to care for, girls who had their entire lives ahead of them.

Her girls needed her.

As they'd gotten older, they sometimes seemed more like friends than her babies. They had grown so quickly into their little personalities, eagerly awaiting the freedom and agency of their teenage years.

She wondered who they would be. Would they choose motherhood as she had? Would they be strong-willed like Ebinimi, graduating early and traveling halfway around the world to a place they'd never heard of before? Would they choose medicine or engineering or art or architecture? Perhaps they had picked up more of her own interest in music than the others—they loved to make up little songs and dance around to them.

Regardless of who they chose to be, what she hoped—needed— for them was a happy, stable life.

In the absence of her father, Uncle Béla, and Papa, she pushed forward in her determination to raise her youngest daughters with the strong moral compass she had ingrained into their siblings.

As Terike sat by the dining table, coloring a picture of a Disney character, Judit thought she could see the girl as an adult.

"Mommy?" the little girl said, eyes still fixed on the drawing.

"Yes, *kicsikém?*" she said, using a pet name that meant, "my little one."

"You don't have a father."

The child's innocence barely eased the sting of the statement, but she swallowed hard and forced a resolute nod.

Looking up from her coloring, Terike rested her chin in the palm of her hand. "How can you live without your father?"

Judit went to the girl, then, aching to pick her up, cradle her in her arms like she had when the girls were small. Instead, she feigned a glance at the girl's picture, and, with an affected casual tone replied, "What made you think of that now?"

"I just can't imagine living without you or Daddy." Terike stood, then, wrapping her arms around her mother. "I would kill myself if you died!"

"No!" she shouted before she could stop herself. The child's comment had been like a sharp punch to her chest. "No," she said again, gentler. "Don't say that. A mother should die before her child." Wary that her sharp response may have rattled the child, she stooped down to eye level with the girl. "You will be able to live without me."

As silence settled around them, Terike just nodded.

Chapter 25

CHAMBERS

———

RAIN PELTED THEIR UMBRELLAS, A restless percussion that urged them forward to their destination. With pangs of nostalgia for times past, Matthew trekked through the cemetery, Obi following close behind, squinting at the sea of tombstones until they reached the marker with the great man's name etched on its side.

Albert Koós. Judit's father.

Having already visited Béla Bartók's grave to pay his respects to the famous composer, he felt the chill of wetness seeping into his clothing. Matthew's feet sunk into the mud, a trickle of wetness touching his sock where the sole had begun to split. Focused on their task, he ignored the discomfort.

Standing silently, he looked down at the well-trod burial plot as Obi fidgeted next to him.

His son hadn't understood why he was willing to venture out in the rain, just to visit the cemetery. As he sensed himself moving into a new phase in life, he found himself sentimental at times, reflecting on all that he'd accomplished—and all that he hadn't. His political venture hadn't yet yielded much success, and JUMA—despite limited advances—had ultimately ended with little profit. Matthew hoped that this reflection on life and living would help guide him forward.

After a long, silent pause, he looked over at his son. Obi's gaze was fixed in the distance, distracted, likely by his own life—now in medical school, he was a man now. Matthew remembered that time in his own life well, everything full of promise and possibility.

It was impossible not to be proud of his oldest children, all three building new lives for themselves far away from Judit, their little sisters, and him.

On this trip, another point of pride struck him.

This time, he could finally afford to support them with their university education, just as he'd always imagined he would. As they sat down to dinner to celebrate the two boys' birthdays, he could feel the roll of money in his pocket, and he couldn't wait to see their faces when he produced it. He'd dreamed that one day he would be in a position to help his children this way. With each new failed venture, with each new need brought to him by his family in the villages, that dream had faded.

Not that he resented sharing his money with his family. Compared to them, he and Judit lived extremely comfortable lives. It was his duty, then, as was common in Nigerian families, to periodically send them money along with advice for what they should buy with it—2,000 naira for dried fish, 550 for a tin of palm oil, 250 for ogbono seeds—and any other necessities he knew they needed.

When it came to these things, there really was no choice. He was not only expected to have a responsibility toward his wife and children but also toward his parents and siblings—all were family. All needed support.

He'd wanted to give more than just support, too. A while back, he'd bought land in Tombia, a relatively large plot that would house a mansion, a guest house, and a boys' quarters—perhaps, he'd thought at one point, he and Judit might retire there, his father taking the guest house and the children and other family visiting whenever they chose. At one time, they'd made a few improvements to the property.

In that version of his future, he'd achieved so much, growing the family's wealth while refusing to participate in the corruption of so many Nigerian company managers and politicians. He'd successfully helped his people in that imagined life—not only his family, but all of Rivers State. An influential and highly respected politician, he would have ushered in the change he'd imagined as a younger man. But as time had crept forward, many of those dreams had fallen by the wayside.

For one thing, his political career had toppled.

Perhaps it was better that way. After all, while he hadn't succeeded in leading the SDP to gubernatorial victory, he'd left the political arena with his freedom and his life.

That was more than many Nigerian leaders could say.

Just the previous November, a bloodless coup led by Defense Minister General Sani Abacha had ousted the interim president. Abacha, a short man—with something of a Napoleon complex—had long tribal scars on his face, the deep, dark lines running the length of each cheek. A threatening figure, particularly with his penchant for dark sunglasses, Abacha had very particular viewpoints on how the country should run.

After General Ibrahim Babangida annulled the June presidential election—a process Matthew knew intimately from the heartbreak it had caused him and the other SDP leaders—the country's leadership had fallen to Chief Ernest Shonekan, a highly educated lawyer with wire-rimmed spectacles who slid seamlessly between Western business attire and the traditional clothing of his Yoruba tribe.

Despite Shonekan's intellectual credibility, military leaders had found him lacking—or, more precisely, one particular military leader had found him lacking.

Just months after he assumed the role of interim president, the scar-faced Abacha had toppled his government, seized Nigeria, and placed the country once again under military rule. The two political parties, SDP and NRC, were dissolved. Abacha then decreed his own power, granting himself the right to imprison anyone he saw fit for up to three months.

The writing was on the wall. If politics had been a viable path for Matthew, that was certainly no longer the case. Without politics, what did he have?

He'd known that politics wasn't the most lucrative career path. Despite the way the villagers looked at him—cheered for him, even—he'd taken home relatively little money. He'd been proud of that, in a way. His most consistent platform was that he'd entered the political arena determined to fight against fraud. Unlike so many wealthy Nigerian politicians, he refused to line his pockets from the public coffer.

He'd worked in the private sector during his time with Shell and in the public sector during his ill-fated tenure with WAGI and, shortly after, with Waterglass Boatyard. Neither of those had provided much security, the payments irregular at best and comparatively meager when they did come regularly.

So what would he do now?

What *could* he do now?

"Apu?"

Obi's question shook him out of his daydream, and he returned to the dinner table in Hungary to see both of his oldest boys staring at him. "Eh, what is it?"

His son looked puzzled. "I asked, where are you working now?"

At that, Matthew unleashed a signature chuckle, finally withdrawing his wallet from his pocket. "There are big things happening," he said. "After this trip to Taiwan—" he let the air fall silent for a moment. "Everything will be fine."

As he handed the cash—two thousand US dollars—across the table, Tonye's eyes went wide. That felt good.

A boy should be proud of his father.

In truth, the money from the Taiwan deal hadn't come through yet. He knew it would if they just gave it time, but for the moment, his and Judit's accounts stood at close to zero.

His new business partner, Lee, had loaned him the money. The Chinese man was as confident as Matthew that the deal would close soon. He'd met Lee only a short time before, but the two had connected immediately. Where Matthew struggled with brokering deals despite his academic and social strengths, Lee brought an entrepreneurial brilliance to the partnership. Together—with Matthew's charisma and Lee's business savvy—they were the perfect team.

So as he handed the money to his sons—a gesture that seemed much too casual given the weight of such a gift—he reassured himself that he was making the right choice. With Lee in the picture, there would be plenty more where that came from.

He thought his father would have been proud. As a preacher, he'd taught Matthew the importance of integrity—of standing up for the underdog and pushing to make things better. He'd lived by those principles his entire life because, although he hadn't always loved his father's lessons, he respected their purpose.

His father had been unflinchingly strict with him. Ever present in his childhood home—in most of his friend's homes, too—the long, slightly flexible cane used for flogging children when they misbehaved was always in view.

The lessons that stuck with him most had less to do with the cane. When he thought of his father's lessons, he remembered the marbles.

He'd failed to complete his homework one day. His father had warned him before that there would be consequences of such an oversight, but he hadn't obeyed, probably caught up in some childhood game he couldn't remember.

So his father had taken his only possession, a set of shiny, colorful marbles, and burned them in the fire.

He understood, now, why the man had taken them—the lesson, of always completing the work that was due, had carried him far. Though at the time, the pang of loss had stung; the uncontainable burst of frustration so central to childhood punishments.

Other lessons were more pleasant to remember, as when Matthew had insisted on carrying fish to school for a snack but, having no lunch pail, he'd shoved the meat in his pockets. His father had ordered him not to do it again and, for a time, he'd complied. When he next got the idea to carry fish in his pockets, his father had taken his pants and sliced the pockets open.

"But I can't put anything inside!" he'd wailed.

"Correct," his father had said matter-of-factly. "You will learn your lesson."

He'd tried to listen from then on. The story was a family favorite now because his children found the thought of stuffing one's pants with fish endlessly hilarious. It stuck with him in a way that was more than simply funny. It reminded him of how his father had taught him discipline.

Wanting so badly to make his father proud, his people proud—and he hoped he had succeeded at that—he'd aimed high and shot high.

He hadn't always been perfect. But he'd always tried.

The older he'd gotten, the more he'd begun to realize that trying was really all anyone could do. He'd relearned that lesson with every new business venture, every new deal, and every new opportunity. Sometimes the things that looked less probable came through. More often, the things that looked the most certain cost you the shirt off your back.

When things went south like that, all you could do was stand through the pain and keep on walking. There was no sense going backward. No sense in dwelling on the unfortunate circumstances behind you.

He tried to explain that to Judit as the two sat combing through the growing stack of unpaid bills. She'd once been enthusiastic about his new ventures, but she was more difficult to persuade now. She'd been there with him as each new opportunity had fallen short, as each new check failed to arrive, and each new investment added to their debt rather than relieving it.

If she could just hold on, he'd explained, this partnership with Lee could be a game changer. He had his eye on retail now—he'd even started a small convenience store where they sold household essentials like toothpaste and batteries. People always wanted that kind of thing. A business like that couldn't fail.

Doubt in her eyes, Judit had nodded and sighed, suggesting they use the small remaining balance in their accounts to pay part of what they owed to NEPA. They couldn't cover it all. In truth, it had been nearly a year since they'd last been able to bring the balance on their bill ledger to zero. But they could demonstrate their good faith effort by making a payment, however small.

They'd sat in silence for a few moments, as he considered saying what they both knew aloud—that paying NEPA would mean another month of missing their rent. But some things don't need to be spoken. With nothing to be done about it, it seemed kinder to leave that truth unsaid.

Judit had stood from the table then, gathering the bills and notices into a crumpled pile, each document mangled from months of handling, the accumulation of empty promises curling the edges of each page. Matthew had remained there as he watched the sun set out the window, wondering if he was crazy to believe that things would get better.

They simply had to.

Matthew clung to that belief all night. The next day, he went about his business, checking ledgers and typing away at the paperwork for their new venture, then faxing it—with the lingering excitement of the new piece of office equipment they'd acquired—to Lee in Lagos. The next day, he'd ventured down to the convenience store, scoping out the customer base and observing the way they moved through the store.

Things could be better there, he thought. Perhaps he would rearrange a few of the displays to bring some of the more frequently purchased goods toward the front.

A third, fourth, and fifth day passed that way, Matthew going about his business, a familiar sense of optimism settling into his chest.

As he sat down to business the next day, planning the hours ahead after the girls had made their way to school, five sharp knocks pierced the morning's peace. He reached the door before

Judit, racking his brain for who he might find on the other side. When he opened it, the estate manager wore a grimace.

"Ah, Doc," he said, looking uncomfortable and vaguely aggressive. "We have to get the rent today!"

Matthew swallowed hard, a heavy pit forming in his stomach. "I know. We will have the money very soon. Give us just—"

"No." The man's face had morphed from discomfort to impatience. "We have given you many warnings. Until you can pay, you have to leave."

He felt Judit's presence behind him then, and when he turned to her, her face looked ashen.

"Just a few more days—"

"No," the man said, stern. But as his gaze drifted over Matthew's shoulder to Judit, he softened. "You have to leave before tomorrow."

At that, the man turned and strolled away, having transformed the morning's silence from a peaceful reprieve to an eerie, looming threat.

Judit turned, too. Without saying a word, she walked silently back to the bedroom and he heard her slide the suitcase from its place in the closet and place it on the bed, followed by the rattle of hangers. Matthew's feet seemed frozen in place.

For some time, he stood there—he couldn't say how long—until her voice broke through the stillness, sounding too loud and too calm. She was beginning to discuss the most suitable place to take refuge without sacrificing their pride and reputation.

"Maybe Miriam," she said.

Again, the terrible silence settled around them.

He heard her take a breath before starting again. "I am sure we can stay with Miriam."

An American from Maine, Miriam Isoun was known in her

work for her efficiency and resourcefulness, and she and Judit had been quite close for a time. The family was relatively stable if not especially well-off. She'd co-authored a cookbook, for which they had a computer before most families in the area. Like Matthew, her husband, Turner, was Ijaw. He was Vice Chancellor of a major university in Port Harcourt.

He'd succeeded.

The thought turned Matthew's stomach.

"Yes," he said, the word sounding dumb and weak to his ears.

Judit called her friend who, being the most pragmatic of the Nigerwives, was happy to be offered a material way to help. After he and Judit had tossed some clothing for themselves and the girls into the suitcase, they walked with heavy steps away from the only home their daughters had ever known and made their way to the Isoun's house.

He tried not to think too much about the raw, desperate humiliation he felt. There was a nagging, spiteful voice in the back of his mind that told him he'd let his daughters down, failed his wife, and embarrassed his entire family.

He was supposed to be the hope of his people. What had that gotten him? After years of standing up for what was right—of fighting for reform—this was what he got. It seemed crushingly unfair.

Still, in his heart, he knew he'd been right in his response to Obi. Something big was coming—he could feel it in his bones. So when the voice rang in the back of his mind, the voice that told him his dreams were over, that he would never find work or close deals while he was sleeping on the floor of his wife's friend's spare bedroom, he clenched his jaw and held to what he knew to be true.

This would all be over soon. He just had to stay optimistic.

With an irony of the caliber that poets only dreamed of, the answer came.

He was invited to lead an ad hoc committee to investigate fraud in the Port Harcourt Chamber of Commerce, Industry, Mines, and Agriculture. The Chamber had been embroiled in a scandal for some time. Membership dues had mysteriously gone missing, leading the bank to seize the Chamber's deposit. As a result, members began to withhold their payments, unwilling to shell out good money to an organization that had proven itself untrustworthy.

The situation demanded an intervention. Without an investigation, there was no way to really understand what had happened, and without understanding the full scope of the issue, they couldn't reasonably ask members to extend their financial support in the future.

So now, Matthew, a man who was known for despising corruption—a man who was currently homeless because anti-fraud ethics didn't pay—was asked to helm the investigation.

This was what he'd been waiting for—he felt certain of it. A chance to rebuild his name as a community leader. This was an opportunity to invest in working with the "Chambers," as people informally called the organization, perhaps even helping the group to dig itself out of the shambles it was in.

Without a second thought, he accepted the role.

The investigation turned out to be relatively straightforward. After questioning those who had worked with the Chambers' former president, Mr. Wopara, and combing through the Chambers' financials, Matthew clearly saw the trail of abuse.

There were counterarguments, of course. Mr. Wopara claimed the accounting officer forged his signature on the application, but there was no evidence of this. The accounting officer also stated Wopara instructed him to inflate most of the checks.

Inflated checks were relatively easy to spot once they knew what to look for. By padding small expenditure bills, Wopara had skimmed a total of 376,282 naira from the Chambers' budget.

It was a shocking amount for the organization, which was supported almost exclusively by membership dues. It was even more shocking for Matthew, who could have paid off every debt in his family's name with that amount of money.

Despite what he knew he could do with an amount like that, Matthew felt vindicated in his anti-corruption stance. Mr. Wopara had lived like a king for some time, and, unfortunately, Matthew knew it was likely he would get away with the fraud, even after being found out.

As the committee issued their final ruling—demanding that Wopara, the financial secretary, and the accounting officer collectively refund the sum plus accrued interest—the former president's fraud created a new window of hope for Matthew.

The Chambers needed a new president.

Perhaps it should be him.

The role—along with the work he and Lee were beginning across Asia—could be the family's salvation.

Of course, even if he were elected president, the pay from the Chambers wasn't much. Still, some monthly income, along with the connections he could make leading the organization, might be enough to finally put the family on stable footing once again.

He decided then that he would run, and while certainly this election was nothing compared to the sprawling campaigns he'd orchestrated as Rivers State Chairman of the SDP, he knew a good deal about politics—even the politics of a private-sector group like the Chambers.

After a few weeks of asking influential Chambers members for their support—weeks that allowed him to gather enough money to move his family back into their home—Matthew emerged victorious.

Not only were they able to leave the Isoun's home, gracious and thankful, but happy to return to their own house—he would also be the new president of the Port Harcourt Chamber of Commerce, Industry, Mines, and Agriculture.

Finally, he'd gotten his foothold and, within a few months, a change would come. He knew it.

He just had to get his family on board. With a full, unflinching belief that they could conquer anything they set their minds to, he sat with Judit to make a new plan for their future. Things wouldn't be easy, at least not for a while—sacrifices would have to be made—but the family could join together as a team and pull themselves out of this situation.

Teamwork wasn't always easy, and it wasn't always fun. But just as his father had taught him difficult lessons all those years ago, he, too, had a responsibility to teach his children about the world.

So one evening, just a few days before Christmas, he called Marika and Terike into the living room.

"Girls," he said. "I need to have a serious conversation with you."

Their little brows furrowed with worry, but they obeyed, sitting as he instructed and staring up at him.

As he faced them, looking them straight in their eyes as he would two respected colleagues, he delivered the news. "You girls are big girls," he addressed them. "So I need to tell you that we are not going to buy any Christmas presents this year."

The way they looked at him, with a concern that he sensed was as much for him as it was for their own gifts, broke his heart. And yet, he pressed forward, hoping they knew that this decision was made out of love—out of hope for a better future.

He thought they might ask questions, that one of them might ask, "why?" Instead, they simply stared up at him.

"We don't have any money," he continued, filling the silence.

The silence seemed to transport him back to that terrible day when the five loud raps came at the door. Finally, Terike broke it.

"It's okay, Apu," she said. "I didn't want any presents anyway."

He feared the words might crush him under their enormous weight. It was not just the disappointment of being a father who couldn't afford to give his children gifts. Even more than that, those words brought a realization—his baby daughters were no longer babies.

And they were all going to be okay.

Chapter 26

AFRICAN SUMMER

⟨⟩

ENERGY BUZZED AROUND THE SPACE and children's laughter danced in the air, the sweet sound set against a hum of eager curiosity.

"See how beautiful my own is!" one little girl exclaimed, her beaded mini-twists whipping to the side as she leaned over to show another child her freshly dyed egg.

"Oooh," her companion responded. "I really like it!"

"What color is your own?"

The second child leaned forward to peer into her small bowl, tucking a sandaled foot underneath her. "It will be green," she replied. "I will leave it inside a longer time." She looked over at her new friend and added, matter-of-factly, "so it will get darker."

The little girl's beads bobbed as she nodded emphatically, and Judit couldn't help but approach the two, beaming at their sweet, innocent confidence as she placed her hands encouragingly on their shoulders.

"These are very pretty!" she complimented the girls, and both looked up at her, grinning with pride.

Glancing across the multi-purpose room, she saw Matthew engaging a table full of children in a lesson on the rules of chess. She strolled over to them, listening quietly as he explained to a little boy with a short afro that, while rooks can move horizontally or vertically, pawns can only move directly forward.

The child's furrowed brow transported her back to the days when her own boys were small, leaning forward with enchantment as their father explained the complicated game. They'd been so eager to impress their father—to master the complex set of rules—and so delighted when they finally beat him.

She saw that same thrill on the faces of these children—more than thirty of them by her count—as they learned how to embroider handkerchiefs and stir ingredients in a stew. With wide, eager eyes, they gathered around music lessons and acting activities, shaped little animals out of colored plasticine, and spread paint onto huge sheets of white paper.

They giggled and laughed and made new friends.

Most importantly, they learned. They'd spent three-and-a-half weeks engrossed in new ways to explore the world. When their parents picked them up, the children rambled on about the day's discoveries, their new knowledge pouring out in a symphony of joy.

"Mommy, we learned a new song today!"

"Did you know spiders have eight legs, but mosquitoes and cockroaches only have six?!"

"Auntie Ifeoma, come and see my painting!"

The adults all smiled, the children's enthusiasm infectious and adorable.

And Judit had made it all happen.

When the idea had first struck her, it almost seemed far-fetched—a vague vision of a project more than a fully formed plan. Years ago, her boys had attended a summer camp in Hungary when they were only ten years old, and they loved it. They had traveled to Zamárdi—a town near Lake Balaton—for a few weeks and had gotten to go on little field trips, learn new things, engage in new experiences, and meet new people.

It had sparked such imagination in them!

While she knew the children of Port Harcourt were getting a quality education, she wished she could show them a different way of learning, too—a way that centered on fun and play and allowed them to use their creativity.

She'd always tried to bring that approach into her own home. As her own children sat at the dining table working on homework, she'd tutor them, employing the energy and physical excitement she'd once hoped to use as a music teacher.

Children didn't get that kind of active learning in their schools here—it simply wasn't the preferred style.

When the schools took breaks between sessions, children had few opportunities for structured activities. Many of them stayed home watching television or playing around the house.

So she'd hatched a plan to put on a "summer" camp—though Nigeria only had a dry season and rainy season instead of the four she'd experienced in Hungary—to bring the experience to Port Harcourt's children! By charging the families a small fee and pooling that money together, they could offer a wide range of topics and activities. And maybe she could bring in a little money for her own family in the process!

At first, she hadn't been sure of where to host the camp. After visiting a few sites, she landed on the Montessori school—a perfect space, given that Montessori's method allowed children to explore the things that interested them rather than follow a set curriculum.

Since Baerbel, a friend of Judit's, was the principal of the school, the school's administration had agreed.

From there, she'd started to organize. There were teachers to recruit, flyers to circulate, decorations to gather, registrations to document, and so many ideas to sift through.

Several weeks later, a parade of children burst through the doors of the school, eager for the programming she'd painstakingly planned. The event's success had been phenomenal.

As the parents ushered their children out after the daily activities one day, the children bubbling over with accounts of the day's activities, several parents had stopped her at the door.

"You must do this again next year," one mother said, taking both of Judit's hands in hers. "The children are learning so much. They love it!"

Behind the woman, another mother joined in the praise. "Yes, they are always so excited to come here!"

"Thank you," Judit replied, a happy blush warming her cheeks. "I am very happy to hear it."

They weren't just being kind—their praise was genuine and well-deserved.

And they hadn't even seen the grand finale!

Wanting the children to perform for their parents, Judit had sat down to pen a play that the campers could all help produce. She settled on a dramatization of Snow White, chosen for its wide range of roles for little aspiring actors. With the sprawling collection of dwarves, everyone could have a part that suited their personality.

And the kids had sparkled in their roles! One child had enacted the role of "Dopey," loping across the stage in a way that sent waves of laughter across the audience. Another gave a bold portrayal of the witch, her high-pitched laugh cuter than it was menacing but with the impressive commitment of a serious actor, nonetheless.

And—Judit could hardly believe it!—the best scenes had been documented by NTA, the Nigerian Television Authority. Out of the blue, they'd showed up at the school just in time for the play's opening. A crew including men with lighting equipment, a journalist, and a videographer carrying a large camera over his shoulder waltzed into the room to broadcast the play. The children had been elated, peaking at the crew as the parade of cameras and equipment trailed into the back of the room.

At the helm of it all was Judit. Bursting with pride, she watched as the children presented a flawless production of her script, parents laughing and whispering at the enjoyment of seeing their children act out the story.

She'd never felt so accomplished.

With it had come an urge to express herself. It had propelled her into this camp—the greatest professional accomplishment of her life so far—and that achievement had only stoked the fire of her creativity.

They'd gotten a new computer—that had helped, too. As soon as they'd set up the machine, her mind overflowed with ideas. She'd begun with writing a series of poems and short stories. Then her mind had turned to children—teaching—and she began writing a series of Catholic children's books, materials that could help children learn the important tenets of the religion, but always in a fun, engaging way.

Often, she sat to type her own thoughts and feelings, too, the words grounding her—centering her—as she moved into this new stage of her life.

It was fascinating how the ideas came, traveling from her mind to her fingers to the glowing pixels on the screen. Just as interesting was how the act of creating gave voice to thoughts that had been buried in her mind—thoughts she couldn't have articulated if not for the form and the music of the language as it materialized on the monitor.

She looked forward to these quiet moments of reflection, the nostalgia of the passion and academic skills she'd honed in her younger years mingling with her dreams of the future. As she considered it, she wrote,

> *"I'm lost between*
> *The rhythm of drums and piano.*
> *In the midst of the logic, I was thirsty*
> *For the freedom in dreams and emotion.*
> *And I felt at home in Africa,*
> *The fertile and bare land was my home soon.*
> *Even we don't believe in reincarnation.*
> *But in the midst of the chaos and destruction,*
> *I am thirsty now for logic and order.*
> *Some say it is only home sickness."*

Life between two homes was funny that way. In her adopted home of Nigeria, she had found such beauty. She'd raised her family here, grown in her relationship with her husband, and built new friendships. Over the years, some from her circle had passed, as with her sweet friend Rosemarie.

Others had come into her life anew. One of the Nigerwives, Angie Ehimika from Liberia, had become a very close friend of hers. Dark-skinned and thin-framed, Angie had three children, her eldest daughter the same age as the youngest Mamah girls. Angie came to the house a lot, always listening when Judit shared the struggles of their lives over the past year. When they talked, she felt her burdens lifted, the weight of life's challenges shared with another, the way she had always tried to do for others, but that she had never had for herself.

Then there was Priscilla Okonny, who lived across the street. Her daughter, Mosep, was ten years younger than Marika and Terike, who loved to pretend the toddler was their younger sister. The girls liked that Priscilla did not talk down to them, conversing instead as if they were her friends. Where Angie had provided a listening ear, Priscilla gave her an opportunity to share about her daughters—to give and receive advice about parenting.

The older Judit got, the more she realized that different relationships offered different types of comfort and support. God had been good to grant her friendships with these kind, helpful, and supportive women, each with their own strengths.

When she answered the telephone one afternoon to hear Ebinimi's voice, she realized that her daughter had grown up to be one of these strong, brave, caring women, too.

They couldn't talk long—her daughter was getting ready for her morning classes and international calls could get expensive very quickly. Always content to hear about the young woman's life halfway around the world, she simply listened as her daughter shared a funny story about a campus event she'd attended and gave an update on her grades.

Since Ebinimi had moved to America, they had checked in regularly this way. Judit kept the family's most difficult afflictions to herself, unwilling to burden her daughter with the family's difficulties when Ebinimi was on an adventure of her own.

Even though they were separated by a great distance, she was proud that they'd remained close. She'd been through this before, after all, when they'd lived in Manchester and still now with her family in Hungary. With a little diligence and effort, one could maintain communication with only infrequent visits.

But that didn't mean she would overlook a chance for an in-person reunion. So when Matthew's new business prospect began to flourish, increasing the family's financial stability, she seized the opportunity to purchase three tickets to Budapest for her and the twins. Ebinimi also purchased a ticket to meet them.

She hadn't realized how badly she needed the reunion until the dates were set! Before she knew it—although the time felt long as she waited anxiously to see her older children—she would be with all five Mamah children together in her home country.

Heart thumping with anticipation, she'd expected to be met with the warmth and love of family—yet she found something even more wonderful as she embraced them for the first time in years. Here, among those who loved her, she felt more at peace than ever before.

This visit was more special than many of the family's previous visits to Hungary, as it fell on Judit's favorite holiday. Spending Christmas in the Zsombolyai apartment filled her with insurmountable joy. It reminded her of the holidays she'd experienced as a little girl. Her mother greeted the family with warm food and smiles, just like she had every Christmas. Some things had changed, though. At ninety, her mother's gray hair had turned a bright white, and the trinkets that lay around the apartment, even freshly dusted, didn't shine as well as they had used to—a reminder of the time that had passed.

Nevertheless, excitement still flowed out of Judit as it always had this time of year.

The first night, the family went to the cinema, a treat for the little girls and an opportunity for a family outing everyone could enjoy. As the family sat, lined up in a single row of the theater, she glanced at her children's faces, illuminated by the glow of the screen.

But it was her own eyes that welled with tears when the film's signature song played. Crooning "God Help the Outcast," the film's heroine seemed to speak directly to Judit's heart. This, Judit remembered, had always been her calling, to stand up for the underdog—for the people. Nostalgic and sweet, the song called to her heart, reminding her of who she'd once hoped she would become—who, she hoped, she had become.

Her heart ached for Esméralda, realizing that the Gypsies of Hungary had long faced discrimination. At times, she'd felt so much like Esméralda—misunderstood, frightened, and hopeless. She, too, had looked to Mary for comfort, trusting that the Holy Mother would watch after her.

Religion had always been a comfort for her, but the weight of loneliness still weighed heavy on her shoulders. She stood out both visually and culturally among her Nigerian neighbors. She knew well the fear of senseless violence enacted against those who were different—it had gripped her heart the night Tonye had returned from work, bloody and bruised.

She continued to reflect, thinking about how, as a child in the Zsombolyai apartment, she never could have imagined what her life would become. But she knew now, without a doubt, that she'd faithfully followed God's path.

There was much to celebrate; little to mourn.

Her beautiful daughter was turning twenty-one years old—an adult, like the boys nearly two years before her. As they sat in the living room of that familiar apartment, the same place they'd sat all those years ago as she and Matthew tried to convince her father to support their relationship, her siblings filed in, one after another.

Bori came first, bearing a beautiful homemade cake. After a round of greetings, each of them kissing the others' cheeks, Bori sidled up next to Judit, draping her arm on her waist.

"You look beautiful, Jutka," she whispered, a quiet, sweet, shared moment among sisters.

In truth, she felt beautiful. She'd taken her daughters to the beauty shop earlier that day—a little treat for the girls while the boys were caught up in the things that occupied college boys. As the hairdresser guided her head back into the basin, she'd closed her eyes, savoring the warm comfort of the water as it trickled down her scalp, the calming pressure of the beautician's fingers massaging her crown. She could hear her daughters chatting and giggling, catching up on all the things they'd missed while they were separated by a vast ocean.

"Hold this here," the hairdresser had requested, guiding Judit's hand to the plush, squishy towel she'd wrapped around her head. "And let's go to the chair."

Judit complied, relaxing into the feeling of being pampered— the feeling of, for the first time in a long time, relinquishing all responsibility and control to someone else.

"Anyu," Marika said, grabbing Judit's hand. "You look so happy."

"I am happy," she replied.

With the siblings gathered together for Ebinimi's birthday that night, Bori must have seen that happiness, too—in truth, Judit knew she radiated it. Although it seemed strange to admit, she felt truly beautiful.

Her children had far exceeded the family's expectations as well, a situation that she knew reflected well on her parenting. When, nearly a quarter century earlier, she and Matthew had sat in this living room with Uncle Béla and her parents, they'd been certain they could build a good life together, but they hadn't dreamed of the success that would smile down on their family. There had never been a doctor in the family before. Now, both Tonye and Obi were progressing well through medical school—Tonye with only a year remaining, and Obi close on his heels with two. Ebinimi seemed well on her way to a promising career in America. The little girls were beautiful and happy, bubbling with energy and lighthearted laughter.

A light squeeze on her shoulder brought her back to the birthday celebration, and as she looked around, she realized that every one of her siblings was present, together. She couldn't remember the last time they had all gathered. Potyi had distributed glasses of wine around the room, including to Ebinimi who, now old enough to drink even in America and well within the requirement in Hungary, enjoyed a toast with the family.

That beautiful girl, her daughter, nearly glowed in the center of the room. To her right, Tonye stood quietly, always the more reserved sibling, handsome in his sleek black turtleneck. And Obi, always the silly one, hovered at Ebinimi's side, joking and teasing her about one thing or another, his eyes bright and joyful. The little girls wove and darted about the room, content and safe among the many people who loved them.

Laughter filled the apartment, the chatter of a big, overflowing family-like music in the air, and Judit felt suddenly called to step forward.

"*Boldog, boldog, boldog születésnapot,*" she sang, the first line of a Hungarian birthday song. Glancing around at her siblings, her gaze a subtle invitation to join, she started again. This time, the entire family raised their glasses to one another and to the birthday girl. "*Kívánjuk hogy legyen még sok ilyen szép napod!*"

Together, they sang.

Judit would reminisce on the trip the entire way back to Port Harcourt. So glad for the visit away from all of the stresses of life in Nigeria, she was still glowing as she greeted Matthew at the airport. Noticing her rejuvenation, he greeted her thoughtfully.

"You look so beautiful, Jutka," Matthew smiled. "I would marry you all over again!"

Chapter 27

SALT AND SUGAR

⁓

I N THE DAYS BEFORE THE coups, Matthew had embraced the wide, sprawling dreams of a boy on the cusp of
manhood. Plenty of his hopes had been for his own life—a
successful career, a family, freedom to explore the world—but he'd
also hoped for political strength for the Riverine Ijaws.

And on October 1, 1996, more than three decades after he'd
first journeyed to Port Harcourt for school, that hope finally materialized. Carved out of Rivers State, a new state was born.

Bayelsa State.

The name, it seemed to Matthew, rang with optimism. Even the
air felt electric, just as it had in the 1960s. He'd fantasized, then, of
parity for his people. And with Yenagoa—a region that included
Tombia, one of Matthew's ancestral towns—named the state capital,
it seemed that his vision would finally be achieved. There were opportunities for roads, electricity, running water, and the prosperous
land that had seemed a fantasy just a few years earlier.

Perhaps Bayelsa State could fulfill another of his dreams. With
no well-known political leaders in Bayelsa, he would be well-suited

for the governorship. Previous experience had taught him to be cautious with such plans—even the most certain Nigerian politician could be toppled with little warning—but he could see his political future in this new state as clearly as his own reflection in the mirror.

For the moment, though, there was little time for political aspirations—for the moment, he had a business deal to close.

As he stepped into the chaos of the motor park, a man rushed by, his shoulder jostling Matthew.

"Lagos, Lagos!" the man called back to him, but already he was disappearing into the mass of people who bustled around to the soundtrack of honking cars. Dodging left and right, men walked between rectangular, white minibuses, some of which bore the scars of previous collisions.

"Ay!" shouted one man in a turquoise-striped polo. "650 naira! Private car!"

Another man dashed past him, nearly colliding with Matthew, as a car horn blared after him. A whirlwind of people weaved through the streets—some in traditional robes and headpieces, some in Western ties and t-shirts, and even some in bathroom slippers.

"Hey!" the man shouted again.

Matthew slipped through the frenetic crowd, his eyes peeled for a minibus. While a private car would always be preferable for comfort, such a luxury was simply not in the budget that day. He could have flown, of course. But air travel in Nigeria was not only expensive but often unpredictable. Flying only when he absolutely needed to, he preferred the safety of the road, but taking the family's green Mercedes would have left Judit without transportation.

So, while the motor parks were unbelievably chaotic, they were well worth the reassurance of safety.

"Two more seats!" a young man shouted, cupping his hands around his mouth.

"Lagos," Matthew responded, raising a hand to the man as he jogged toward the bus.

The man held out his hand. He couldn't have been older than eighteen or nineteen, Matthew guessed.

"150," the man repeated to each potential passenger.

Nodding, Matthew pulled the money from his wallet and handed it over, then climbed aboard the bus. True to the boy's word, the seats overflowed with passengers. Matthew squeezed into a seat in the front of the bus, holding his small travel bag on his lap to maximize space.

The vehicle was hot in the midday sun, but the ride would go quickly. All would be worth it for the prize that awaited at the end.

Not long before, Matthew had stumbled upon an idea.

While Nigeria had no industry to produce salt, its demand was high. Lee Tzu-Lei, his business partner, was well-acquainted with the industry. A quiet, unassuming Chinese man with a modest haircut and greying temples, Lee concealed a wealth of business knowledge beneath his shy exterior. He was the perfect foil for Matthew, who brought charisma and exuberance to their dealings.

When it came to this new venture, they complemented one another in an even more important way—China, where Lee had many high-level connections, was a major exporter of salt, a simple compound that Matthew's extensive chemical engineering training made him particularly well-suited to explore.

The partnership was obvious. Armed with their complementary strengths, they would bring salt production to Nigeria, positioning themselves at the helm of a budding industry. If they were successful, they planned to expand into sugar production as well.

The idea propelled their relationship to a new level. They grew closer and built on one another's strengths. Matthew often traveled to Lagos, where he would stay with Lee, the two strategizing plans and sharing their insights late into the night.

But this trip was different. On this trip, he and Lee would join the team of Nigerian business partners they'd assembled, gathering to sign the final documents to register their new company, MEKEKE. With Lee and an advisory board on his side, he felt confident and powerful, the plan steadying him, even in the midst of the daily commotion. While at times he felt the fatigue of the road in his bones, more often the promise of new possibilities rattled through his body with an untamable energy—a calculated, determined optimism.

That optimism made the business travel tolerable, even exciting, a very good thing given that there was no end to it in sight.

When he'd reached Lagos, Lee greeted him with a warm smile and a firm handshake. They'd signed the papers the next day, a process that made his heart leap in his chest. Then, after delivering Marika's and Terike's passports to the Hungarian Embassy in Lagos for renewal, he and Lee traveled with several business partners to meet Lagos State's military governor and the visiting manager of a salt production factory in China.

Then he'd gone back to Port Harcourt—only for ten days— where he'd pivoted to his Chambers responsibilities. With a very successful year as Chambers president under his belt, he could feel a newfound business savvy rising to meet the threshold of his political success.

He'd brought the organization back from ruin. It was more than even he'd hoped for when he took over the floundering group. Refusing to allow the Chambers to fail, he'd leapt into the role with fervor, meeting with the Rivers State Military Governor and Commissioners routinely and rallying the group's former and new members until, once again, the dues roll brought Chambers's balance sheet into the black.

Following the announcement of Bayelsa State, he joined with his Chambers colleagues to announce the first joint Bayelsa and Rivers State trade fair, planned for early the next year. The event would be historic, but it meant traveling back from Lagos to meet with the show's planning committee.

With so many different foci, he sometimes felt his mind reeling, crisscrossing between topics just as he zig-zagged across the country.

But there was always more to do—at least for now—and the work would pay off this time. This time, his plans seemed to spread out before him, snaking and joining as the rivers that lined his homeland.

At the thought alone, he could feel his back relaxing, his lungs opening to the warm gulf air of his childhood. What would his homeland be, now that the Ijaw people had their state? Not that Bayelsa was theirs alone, of course. But in a way, it felt as though it was something they could finally own. Or, it felt that way to him, at least.

The thought made him yearn for his childhood—for his mother and his late father. For years, as he and Judit planned to retire to Tombia, he'd dreamed of showing his father the realization of his ambitious building plans on the land he had purchased.

But when his father passed, nothing of the mansion, guesthouse, or boy's quarters were finished.

Now, the guesthouse stood, already occupied by his nephew, the house's caretaker.

As he stood on that land now, admiring the completed building, he could picture, clear as day, how the other two buildings would flank the sturdy home.

This land would soon be his home, closing the circle of his life by bringing him back to his father's region. There, he could enjoy a quieter life—certainly quieter than his current travel schedule—while advancing some of the goals he'd carried with him for years.

Just that day, in fact, he registered with NECON, the National Electoral Commission of Nigeria, to concretize his intention to rejoin politics as a part of Bayelsa State's inaugural leadership. He had previously written to the Military Governor for a position in his cabinet.

At his side, the Tombian Chief, Christian Otobotekere, confirmed his thought, noting in a clipped, fast-paced patter, "I would vote for no other governor but you."

Matthew nodded at that, as the two men stood admiring the land.

"*Ari opu ye amo miegyini!*" the chief continued. You will do great things!

Matthew wasn't certain whether he meant for the land or the state.

In a way, they weren't so different. He had big aspirations for both.

Key among them was the establishment of paved roads to shepherd the people between villages. While the state's status had changed dramatically in the past few months, its infrastructure had advanced little—if at all—since his childhood.

So just as he had done so often as a younger man, he rented a boat to take him from Tombia to visit his mother in Ogbia.

And just as he had seen so often, she came running from the house, ululating with joy to see him. The children of the neighborhood danced and skipped alongside him as he trekked from the makeshift dock to her house.

He'd built this home, too.

So different from the mud walls of his childhood, this house was constructed in brick and cement, a sight that had once seemed so grand as to be beyond reach. His mother ushered him inside, insisting, as she always did, upon serving him a warm but meager meal of eba with a fish and periwinkle soup.

Except it was no longer his mother cooking.

Instead, his mother eased into a well-worn chair as his younger sister, Ruth, lit the fire and gathered the ingredients.

"Sit," Ruth scolded in a voice that almost startled him in its similarity to their mother's. "You look tired." Instead of taking his seat, he went to where his sister Comfort sat. Ruth blew out a huff of air, shaking her head as she did.

Matthew paid little attention, his focus, instead, on his sister's state. A laugh escaped his lips, and Comfort shot him a wry smile.

"Have you heard from Dorcas?" he asked.

"Yes." She looked him straight in the eye. "She's progressing well. We will have a new baby in the family soon."

Ruth's voice broke from her place at the stove. "*Bo ye fe.* The food is very good."

Matthew followed Comfort over to where Ruth was spooning the thick soup into a simple plastic bowl.

Comfort took the bowl from their sister and returned to her seat at the table.

"*Olowiri onyi,*" their mother said. A boy.

"She says that," Ruth interjected. "I say a girl. The baby sits high on the body." She gestured toward her abdomen.

As Matthew took his own bowl from his sister, the room went quiet for a moment.

"Olowiri onyi," his mother said again softly. "Like my son."

Taking a slow, silent palmful of eba, he looked at his mother, reflecting back on his childhood years in Ogbia. Most had not been easy, not for him nor his sisters.

His mother, most of all, had been tested by their circumstances.

And yet, his childhood had been happy.

They hadn't had much. When he thought about it, that wasn't the part of his childhood he remembered most. It wasn't even near the top of his list. He remembered instead swimming in the rivers' waters, riding alongside his mother in the boat, moments of swift discipline and those of care.

Not long after he left his mother's home in Ogbia, he was back on the road, crisscrossing the country. First, he traveled northward to Kebbi State for a trade fair. Then, to the historic Argungu Fishing Festival several hours away. Days later, he would head south again.

On April 10, 1997, he strode to the special pavilion of Port Harcourt's inaugural Bayelsa and Rivers State Joint Trade Fair.

They'd planned the fair well before the salt deal had been finalized, bestowing the event with the theme, "Towards the Actualisation of a Self-Reliant Economy." Even more fitting, the fair's theme spoke to his goals for MEKEKE. The company would mark an enormous stride toward riverine self-reliance, and later, when the plan's second phase kicked in and sugar production began, Bayelsa would rival even the most prosperous of the Nigerian states.

Or, at least that was his dream.

Matthew's dreams had always been contagious; the ability to

spread positive energy was his most natural gift. As he stepped to the center of the fair to welcome the crowds, he slipped once again into his political aspirations.

They fit like a glove.

After welcoming the Rivers State military governor and other dignitaries—the Bayelsa State governor and the Kebbi State governor would not arrive until later in the festival—a traditional drum corps interjected the booming base that marked the opening of the Nigerian national anthem.

"*Arise, O Compatriots,*" the crowd sang, their voices ascending the scale triumphantly. "*Nigeria's call obey.*" As they sang, Matthew looked around the Port Harcourt Recreation Field, the space overflowing with eager leaders, entrepreneurs, and prospective businessmen and women. He straightened his tunic as the song finished in its flourishing pledge to serve the country with "*freedom, peace, and unity.*"

After a moment of pause in which the final pitches echoed, lingering in the air, he stepped forward.

"The oil-rich city of Port Harcourt is once more alive!" he began, his voice warm but commanding.

The crowd murmured, a few moments of sporadic applause erupting around him.

As the applause melded into the murmur of eager attendees, Matthew stood, poised and self-assured, looking out over the event. In just months, he would turn forty-nine—just one year shy of his jubilee.

He would scarcely pause to celebrate, instead embarking on yet another journey—another step in these new, exciting ventures. While he'd certainly earned a celebration considering all he'd accomplished that year, those very successes made the promise of advancing the country's industry a much more fitting celebration than an evening of focusing on himself.

The MEKEKE company's timeline had been established. Before his next birthday, the salt fields would be in full production with sugar plants soon following. The second annual trade fair would undoubtedly be an even greater success than the first, an impressive feat given the delight he'd seen on the faces of attendees throughout the fair's exhibitions, cultural presentations, and dignitary speeches.

The governmental structure of the new state would be established by then, too, emerging just as he would be preparing to step away from the more active parts of the new company's founding.

If he'd sequenced the next year's moments by design, they couldn't have been any more perfectly arranged.

He'd thought, years ago, that he'd known what it meant to live as his father always instructed. Along the way, he'd enjoyed greater success than he could have ever imagined as that young boy who had fought back tears as his marbles melted in the fire.

The festivals had ignited a new strength in Matthew, and he carried it with him as he and his three new business partners—Alhajis Albishir, Garba, and Idris—departed for Taiwan. The trip would help them build connections and identify everything they needed for a successful operation. They were received at the Taipei airport by Lee and three other business partners. They soon checked into their hotel and met for a grand dinner. As wonderful smells filled the room and plates of spiced meats and vegetables lay before them, the men shook hands and laughed together before turning the conversation to preparation for their business ahead.

First, they toured the Taiwan Sugar Corporation, and Matthew visited with the chairman of Taiwan Finance Corp. The corporation had expressed interest in helping Nigeria forge close relationships with the US—a great advantage to the growing company and Nigeria as a whole. The entire trip overflowed with possibility.

He could see the same optimism on the faces of Lee and the Alhajis as they made their way through the city. Gaudy in their bright coats of paint, figurines of dragons and cats peered at the group through shop windows, the aroma of familiar foods prepared in unfamiliar ways swirled around them, and everywhere, people walked and laughed and talked. Matthew recognized none of their language, but he heard his own excitement in the rhythm of their voices.

"Matthew!" Lee called behind him. "Are you coming? We're going to lunch."

He nodded to Lee and turned to follow him, glancing back once more as he realized what the sight meant.

It meant achievement.

After a brief visit in Hong Kong—where they had been received elegantly in official cars usually reserved for Chinese and Nigerian officials—the group made their way to Beijing. The beauty of the exhibits at the Dingling Museum, the ancient dampness of the Mausoleum of Emperor Zhu Yijun and Empress Xiaoduan, and the echo of righteous rebellion at Tiananmen Square called out their stories—throngs of visitors surrounded by their songs of the past.

Matthew heard the future in the breeze that whistled across the Dinghai salt field. Guided by the team of industry experts, they took salt samples and calculated costs. They questioned timelines and negotiated terms. Not without tension, the talks continued over the next few days, sometimes stalling and restarting, even hiccupping off their tracks periodically.

But they refused to be derailed. By the time the Nigerian High Commissions' two Mercedes limousines arrived to transport the MEKEKE directors to the airport, the deal had been settled. Much work remained, but relatively little of it was unexpected.

The plan Lee and Matthew had built was gaining momentum, chugging forward with the orchestrated harmony of success.

While he knew that business could turn at any moment—he'd experienced it firsthand—he also felt a new calm in his gut, a confidence beyond what he'd felt before.

By the time Matthew turned forty-nine on July 11, MEKEKE was on its way to success. He'd logged over 100 trips since the beginning of the year, viewing the expanse of Nigeria through the dirt-dusted windows of cars and buses. The Ondo State Commissioner had officially authorized documents for a salt production plant—the first of its kind in Nigeria. The several-hun-dred-hectare salt field would initially be established in the Asisa community along the Atlantic coast. A Taiwanese delegation had arrived just a few days earlier to explore sugar production in Niger State.

He would benefit from these deals, and so would his family. Most of all, he imagined how the new venture could elevate the Nigerian people—not just his village or state, but his entire home country. Maybe, through this work, Nigerians would gain the footing he'd long wanted for them. His people would have what they needed, and he would lead them.

Matthew felt more invigorated by this prospect than he ever had with his previous businesses—he had found his calling. With the air of a man who believed he had climbed to the top of a ladder only to find that the rungs continued far above him, he embarked on the next leg of the marathon journey.

In a way he'd never experienced before, he truly understood what it meant to go beyond aiming high and shooting high.

He knew, now, what it meant to land high, the wind at his back as the universe spread its arms wide and embraced him.

Chapter 28

BENIN

"Hi, ev-er-y-body!" Terike spoke, looking into the mirror, trying unsuccessfully to emulate an American accent. "I'm happy to be here," she continued, prolonging the last vowel sound.

Standing back, beyond the girls' line of sight, Judit watched as Marika giggled behind her sister, peering over her shoulder and into the mirror.

"No, not like that," Marika teased. "Hey maaan!" she continued with an animated facial gesture.

Terike nudged her sister playfully.

Unwilling to interrupt the girls' play, Judit stifled her own chuckle and went back into the kitchen to resume her own preparations. The girls could practice their accents—she had packing to do.

Sending a shiver down her spine, her excitement mingled with feelings of anxiety, hope, and nostalgia for the future she'd imagined in Nigeria.

They were going to America.

Since Ebinimi had been there, she'd called home periodically, and Judit loved hearing about her life. While she was concerned about her daughter, it seemed her daughter was just as concerned about her. The young woman had nudged her to consider moving the family to America, promising, for one thing, stable utilities for the family—six months of electrical issues had left them hobbling by on only a gas generator, and the longer Judit went without being able to use multiple appliances at once, the more appealing the move sounded.

Even more exciting, Ebinimi had described new educational opportunities for Matthew. He could continue to pursue higher education there with a funded graduate program, and, while it wouldn't pay much, it would at least be a steady paycheck while the family looked to what they would do next.

As though the girls had read her mind, Judit heard a wave of giggles from the next room, where Terike and Marika were practicing for their American debut. The excitement in the house was palpable.

But Judit also felt a pang of nostalgia. She'd imagined herself retiring in Tombia, on the land Matthew had been developing for them. Perhaps, she'd thought, the boys would move back to their father's country and open a clinic there. She could continue to grow closer to Opumama, Matthew's mother, and build stronger relationships with his sisters. After so many years in Nigeria—years that not only involved raising her children, but that also included accomplishments like the children's program and her leadership in Nigerwives—an anxious tension bubbled up between the excitement of new possibilities and the longing for old dreams.

Matthew, in particular, grew more anxious as the trip approached. They were traveling to the US Embassy in Lagos for a visa interview. They would also stay with Lee on their trip, so he and Matthew could work through a few business tasks. From the first time she'd raised the idea of moving to the United States, something had shifted in his body language. He'd never said no, going along with the plan from the beginning, renewing passports during his many trips to Lagos and taking the needed competency test.

But something lingered below the surface. He seemed tense, resistant, and she worried that she'd pushed him toward a vision that wasn't his. If he went along with a plan he didn't actually support, particularly a plan as life-changing as leaving Nigeria, what would that do to their marriage?

She'd tried to speak with him about it, but found it difficult to get a straight answer—a situation that was somehow even more difficult than an argument would have been. One evening, about three months before the date they had set to leave, the stress and anxiety had gotten to her, and she'd plopped down at the kitchen table and cried.

It had been a stressful day in general. Alongside the overarching nerves that flooded the house, several small things had gone wrong—dinner burned, one of her favorite dresses had snagged, and her task list seemed to grow by two for every one item she completed.

She needed release, and that release came in the form of hot tears and a tightness in her chest as she forced herself to cry quietly in the kitchen, out of her family's sight.

Within seconds, Marika wandered in. Judit quickly wiped her face, flashing a reassuring look at her daughter.

The little girl stopped in her tracks, her face blank. "Anyu?" she asked. "What's wrong?"

She pinched her lips into a tight smile and shook her head. "I'm just worried," she said. Then, hearing in the silence that her daughter expected her to continue, she added, "I don't think Apu wants to go to America."

The moment the sentence escaped her lips, she knew it had been a mistake. Marika's face had turned angry, her eyes flashing, and, before Judit could stop her, the little girl had banged on the kitchen door.

"Marika—" Judit had said, standing and reaching out to the girl.

She was too late. She'd already flung the door open and marched angrily into the living room where Matthew was entertaining some friends. Judit could hardly listen.

He later told her that the little girl had made a scene, scowling at him and slamming the door to the living room. For that outburst, she'd received a slap and a stern warning not to repeat the behavior.

It had been a tense moment.

But it was as though that moment had allowed them all the release they needed. Once they'd gotten things out, they could move forward as a family—these things happened with such major changes ahead.

And they had—since that incident, their family's relationships had been stronger than ever.

While Matthew spent much of his time on the road—sometimes arriving from one trip the same day he needed to leave for another—he had been more open with her than he had been in years. They'd even spoken explicitly about the issue of keeping secrets, and they'd both agreed not to hold things from one another. In housework, too, he'd made a remarkable effort to support her, even retrieving water for her when he was home.

He seemed energized and excited again, too, sharing his big plans over dinner and with neighbors who stopped by.

It wasn't just her marriage that felt stronger. All of her relationships seemed to be flourishing. Having cared for Matthew's mother through her various illnesses—she'd come to stay with the family during a particularly difficult bout of malaria—she'd grown quite fond of the older woman. The care wasn't always easy. A very picky eater, Opumama needed frequent encouragement to take in enough nutritious foods, and she'd never liked taking her medications. But Judit found that the relationship she got in turn—the friendship, even—was well worth the effort.

Then there were the Nigerwives. Paradoxically, just as they were about to leave Nigeria for at least a few years, her relationships with the women in the group seemed to blossom. She'd grown very close with Angie, who had even been attending church with her some Sundays. She'd met many new women from around the world back in March at the annual Nigerwives national meeting. This year's was held in Port Harcourt, at the Shell Camp, where she met Réka Okonkwo.

She and Réka had much in common. Not only were they both Hungarian, but, as they got to know one another, they realized their paths had intersected before—Réka's husband was the pediatric surgeon who had circumcised Tonye and Obi over two decades ago in Budapest! She'd even visited them as newborns. As they'd talked more and more, Judit had felt so connected to her.

So when she shared that her son was a chemical engineer who had moved to Port Harcourt to work on a rig there, she'd insisted that Réka give him their contact information.

"My older children are out of the house," she'd told the woman.

"So if Emeka ever needs a place to stay, or to talk, please tell him to stop by."

Réka had agreed, and, a few months later, just a few weeks before they were to visit the American Embassy in preparation for their move, Judit opened the door to greet her friend's son. He was a thin, young man, biracial like her children, with bright eyes and a welcoming smile.

"*Csókolom*," he said, greeting her in Hungarian.

Before the young man even finished speaking, Judit had broken into an enthusiastic smile, ushering him into her home as he spoke. "*Szia*, Emeka. It's very nice to meet you!" she replied. "Please, come in."

As they chatted, she saw more and more of her own sons in him. He reminded her of when Tonye and Obi had gone off on their own. Knowing how hungry her boys had often been, she had prepared a full lunch for him—a Hungarian stew called *pörkölt* with rice and a cucumber salad.

As the sweet, rich smell of the simmering food filled the room, she asked Emeka all about his life. They discussed his career plans and his experiences in Port Harcourt. They laughed at shared references to Hungarian culture and the shock they'd felt at traveling to Nigeria for the first time. He talked about his difficulties at his job, and Judit suggested he ask Matthew to vouch for him.

When the food was finally ready, she ladled it into two dishes and sat with the boy, laughing and chatting for hours. It was as though Hungary had come to her—her longing for her home soothed by their casual Hungarian conversation and by the joy that filled the room.

Soon, he traveled back to his parents' home in Benin City, another interesting coincidence. Benin City was, after all, about halfway between Port Harcourt and Lagos, where they would eventually board a plane bound for the United States. She wondered whether they might cross paths again.

Just as it had with her and Réka, the universe had a way of bringing people together. Hungarians found one another in Nigeria, and, she was sure of it, they would find Nigerians, Hungarians, and English expatriates in America, too.

She'd been thinking of the beauty that was connection between people for some time. While she continued to pen her short stories and poems, she now found her attention turned to the children's books. Bound by a local print shop, they were a tactile representation of one of her proudest accomplishments, and she loved to run her fingers over the titles on their covers: *The Way of the Cross* and *Hail Mary and the Holy Rosary: Explanation and Illustration for Children.*

The latter book she found particularly important. Children didn't always understand the important role women played in Catholicism, so focusing on the Holy Mother was her way of encouraging children to explore the interesting elements of gender within the religion. She hoped it would inspire her own daughters, too.

A third book would come later—*The Advent Calendar*—but, for now, Judit's mind was focused on the world's cultures. She was fascinated by music's ability to bring people together, condensing so many different sounds, experiences, and feelings together in one, standardized notation system. So she'd turned her attention to a children's music training book. Inspired at least in part by the ethnomusicologic leanings of Bartók and D^2P^2, her high school music teacher, it would include songs from around the world, including countries familiar to her—Nigeria, England,

and Hungary—as well as those she'd only dreamt of. The book overflowed with folk music from Bantu speakers and Himalayan tribes, and places as distant as Jamaica, Germany, Brazil, and, of course, America.

"Aunt Comfort is here!" Marika called from the front door.

Judit stood from her seat at the computer desk and, grinning from ear to ear, made her way to the joyful family reunion that included not only Comfort, but her daughter Irene and grandson Osagie as well. As the family scrambled to make last-minute arrangements for their trip, Matthew had asked his sister to come from the village to care for their mother while they were away.

Four generations of Mamahs joined together in the most meaningful visit Judit could imagine.

In the excitement, Irene patted the boy's back, exclaiming, "Osagie! Your mothers in the third degree are all here!"

He looked up at her and smiled, his face an expression of wonder.

At Irene's announcement, Matthew brought out a family tree he'd hand-drawn months ago and showed it to his relatives. He explained the details, including the towns of origin of specific relatives as well as the interesting overlaps and crossovers between spaces and times.

Soon the conversation turned—as they all knew it inevitably would—to the family's impending trip to the embassy in Lagos. Matthew explained that they would need to load the car early in the morning. Irene blurted out, "Uncle, why don't you travel by air?"

Matthew laughed. "Ah, I don't have money nah!"

But Judit knew there was also a more pertinent reason for choosing to travel by road: to protect his family. Just eight months prior in November, an ADC airline flight traveling the same route from Port Harcourt to Lagos had crashed, killing all 144 passengers, validating an existing distrust of airline safety in the country by most Nigerians.

It had rattled the nation, and perhaps Matthew, who often traveled the route between Port Harcourt and Lagos, most of all. He worried about what others would do if they found out the entire family was leaving, about the dangers they could face, about burglary, and even the possibility that an enemy would harm his family out of spite.

His fears were given some validation when, just ten days earlier, Matthew had been attacked by the Chambers Vice President. The two had been in a meeting with a third associate when the conversation went sour. Later, the VP marched into Matthew's office to continue the confrontation and insulted Matthew before flipping over a glass table in the office, shattering it.

The incident had only exacerbated Matthew's sense of anxiety about what others may do, particularly since he'd reported this to the board and the legal investigation was still ongoing.

Judit had to admit, when she thought of things that way, it made her nervous, too.

More than once, they'd returned home from a trip to find that they'd been robbed. Once, they'd even been robbed while the family was asleep.

So when Matthew had insisted that they keep their travel plans under wraps, Judit had been happy to oblige him. The secrecy, of course, added to the tension of an already tense time, but it was worth it for a small reassurance of safety.

Judit was determined not to let fear interrupt the family's anticipation. She could see much opportunity ahead, days of prosperity and growth filled with exciting new experiences. And beyond her own mindset, she could sense the girls' eagerness for the new adventure. The days leading up to their embassy trip had been full of chatter, the glimmer in their eyes confirming that the move was the right choice. As though it were Christmas Eve, the children's minds seemed to swirl with dreamy possibility.

She could hear their little voices chattering away in whispered tones long after bedtime.

"Go to bed, girls!" she finally demanded. "It's too late to be up."

In a way, she felt like Mikuláš, but rather than leaving candies and nuts for the children, she scurried around ensuring that Comfort and Opumama would have enough food while they were away and that the older woman's medications were properly arranged with detailed directions for dosage and timing.

It was bittersweet, in a way. She'd developed a strong relationship with Opumama, and she couldn't help but wonder how she would fare after they moved. What would happen to the family in Nigeria?

What would happen in the country in general?

She hoped she and Matthew might return to find Nigeria's infrastructure improved. Though it would be a few years before they returned, she prayed that, when they did, they would find that Matthew's years of advocacy had created political momentum, allowing his work to continue even when they were away.

Perhaps it would be like the short story she'd written. "Dream," she'd called it, a story that recounted a beautiful place called "Golden Town." The mythical land in the story had begun as a factory town, developed around the prospect of mining and refining gold. But, at the behest of the brightest scientific minds, the factory's waste had been transformed, as harmful chemicals were channeled into pure carbon dioxide, surrounding the factory with the largest, lushest, and greenest trees.

At the center of the town, people had more than they needed. No longer forced to travel for business, leaving behind their children and wives for hours, days, or even weeks, they could connect through the computer, sending instant mail to one another just as Matthew did with his fax machine, allowing them to collaborate over vast distances.

The vision was so clear in Judit's mind. Roads lined with hand-planted flowers, gardens overflowing with nutritious foods, and families enjoying the gorgeous wooded areas around the town, free from the stress she'd so often felt over the past few years.

Maybe one day, Bayelsa State would be filled with Golden Towns.

Or maybe Golden Town awaited them on the other side of the river—the ocean, really.

The thought comforted her until Sunday morning of July 27, 1997, when it propelled her forward as they loaded the car and climbed in. Matthew sat in front, holding a jerrycan of petrol between his legs—the nationwide scarcity meant sometimes gas was difficult to come by. Judit slid into the back seat with the girls.

Peter, their driver, had recently been promoted, his elevated position carrying with it a new driver's uniform—navy blue pants and a white shirt with blue and white shoulder stripes.

"He looks more like a pilot than a driver," Terike whispered to Judit.

The little girl was right—he did look just like an airline pilot.

As interested as the girls were with Peter's clothing, there were more exciting things that demanded their attention. The Okonnys had emerged from their house, waving and wishing the family farewell, and the girls called out to them, "We will see you soon!"

Several times, Matthew had the car return to the house, feeling as if he had forgotten something. Priscilla Okonny's look turned skeptical until, finally, the car rolled through that familiar red gate. They pulled over then, so Matthew could lead the family in prayer before the family finally drove away from their old home, en route to the United States Embassy in Lagos.

As they did, Judit looked back once more.

That gate had marked the boundary of their home for years. Through the challenging times and the joyful moments, they'd built a life there, raising their children, celebrating their victories, and mourning their losses. It would be difficult to leave the home they'd built together, but Judit turned her eyes toward the road ahead. They proceeded down the Benin-Sapele Road in Benin City.

But just hours later, at 12:50 pm, the family's green Mercedes somersaulted violently, rolling multiple times.

Matthew did not survive the accident.

Judit was loaded into a private car since there were no ambulances.

Along with the two girls, she was taken to the nearest hospital in critical condition, the dream of Golden Town irreparably shattered.

Chapter 29

CALLING

‎〜

EBINIMI HAD LOVED HEARING THE excitement in her mother's voice. Sitting in her apartment in Kansas, it was a comfort to hear from home when she was so far away.

"We will arrive tomorrow night," she'd said, the words clipped and bright, efficient but joyful.

As they'd spoken, she'd heard the girls in the background, the sounds of her little sisters scurrying about in preparation for their Lagos trip.

Then her father was there. She imagined him standing behind her mother. "Tell her we will stay with Lee. Does she have the number?"

Although the question was not directed at her, exactly, she replied, "Yes, I have it."

It was a rare occurrence to speak with her parents two days in a row, and she knew she'd have to keep tomorrow's call short. After five years of international calls, her father's warning played in her ears—"Go off the phone, Jutka! It's expensive!" or "She can't pay!"—a necessary reminder given the price of international calls. Ebinimi typically paid for them and, having little money, she didn't mind her father's conscientiousness, but she also knew how important it was to her mother that she call.

Anyu worried a lot about Ebinimi. Undoubtedly, this was a result of her uncertainty about her daughter's situation—while Tonye and Obi lived with their grandmother in Hungary with family nearby, she was on the other side of the world, alone. With no way for Anyu to call her in America, her mother had to wait for her calls, often expressing enormous relief when she phoned.

Still, their conversations weren't especially rushed or anxious—they talked about a lot of things, but they had to be efficient. She always looked forward to updates on the girls. For example, they were picky eaters, and Anyu thought they might grow up to be entertainers. When she would mention that possibility, Apu would bellow—"What kind of thing are you saying, Jutka?!"—his mind set on professional roles that embodied his more traditional hopes for his children's accomplishments.

Ebinimi had also heard the broad strokes of the family's various struggles and successes—their stay with friends when they had financial difficulties, her father's deepening friendship with Lee, their financial ups and downs, and day-to-day occurrences.

But mostly, her mother wanted to hear about her life.

There was much to tell. During her time in Kansas, she'd seen many exciting opportunities. She'd cobbled together part-time jobs to live on—from waitress to phone operator to resident assistant in the dormitories to camp counselor for at-risk teens. The counselor position had been especially interesting. Since she'd graduated from high school early, she wasn't much older than the teens she supervised, and others at the camp were often surprised to hear that she was a counselor rather than a camper!

She'd excelled in school, transferring from Barton County Community College to the University of Kansas after two years. After completing the credits for an accounting degree, she'd decided to take advantage of her tuition package. She could continue to take additional classes as a full-time student, finishing her pre-med coursework and medical school prerequisites without extra fees.

Her plans for medical school were relatively new. In fact, she hadn't even told her parents yet. She thought about how they would react when she finally told them, revealing that three of their children would be doctors. While she looked forward to sharing the news, she also knew that they were already proud of her. They'd told her so many times.

Still, she was excited to celebrate with them in person. Soon her parents and sisters would join her in America, her father enrolling in a graduate program at her university, and her family living in campus housing.

She'd been surprised that her father had gone along with it. Rather than resisting, he'd completed the paperwork himself for a student visa that would allow them all to move, even if only for a few years. Or maybe it could be longer. In truth, she didn't worry much about that—life could change so quickly, no matter what your plans were.

When she'd called the day before the trip, she'd promised to reach them in Lagos. They hadn't been certain of when they would arrive—likely by Sunday night—but that made little difference in terms of a phone call from around the world. Whenever they arrived, it was likely to be the middle of the day in Kansas.

Dialing the phone, she anticipated a buzz of energy in the background—the twin's chatter, Apu's laughter, or her mother's voice, eagerly anticipating the call.

Instead, she heard only Lee's greeting. "Hello?" His voice sounded hoarse—strangled—as though he'd spent the day sick or shouting.

"Hello! This is Ebinimi Mamah," she said. "I would like to speak to my parents."

She was sure that Anyu would have mentioned their planned call. But where she'd anticipated a quick response—"Yes, here is your mother"—she was met with a thick, wet pause, as though Lee was sniffing hard or even blowing his nose.

Just as she was about to check that he'd heard her, Lee spoke. "I don't know how to tell you…" His thickly accented voice shook as he continued. "There was an accident."

"What?" Her heart thumped against her ribs. Her breaths grew shallow. "Are they…" she swallowed, willing Lee to interrupt. When he made no such move, she forced her voice to be steady. "Are they dead?"

"Your brother and sister are okay."

At this, she paused. Something was lost in translation. That was the only possible answer. Perhaps this was all a misunderstanding. "What about my parents?"

"Not yet," he sputtered out, at a loss for the proper words.

She tried to think for a moment, turning his strange words around in her mind, but her thoughts reeled. What did he mean? A dull, heavy thud repeated in her ears. Her stomach felt upset.

He cleared his throat, and she heard him inhale and exhale deeply. "I will call back when I know for sure."

Resisting the urge to ask him if he was okay, she thanked him and hung up the phone. Panic pulsed through her body. The room around her was deathly quiet. The space too empty. Inside her head, she was screaming.

There had to be some way to get more information. Even if there wasn't, she had to do something. It was as though her energy was larger than her body. And if she didn't act, she might explode.

Hand shaking, she stared down at the phone.

Tonye and Obi. Maybe they could help or provide support.

Dialing the familiar digits—661-161—just as she had dialed Lee a moment before, she felt a hot pinch in her chest. A flash of heat warmed her face.

"Hello," Tonye answered.

She barely waited for his greeting before her fears poured out through the phone line.

"I'm sure they are fine," Tonye responded confidently. This wasn't the first time the family had a scare of losing someone in a car accident, he reminded her. Surely, this would be no different.

But she persisted. With a steady tone that belied the fear that pulsed through her veins, she replied, "I'm really worried about them."

The conversation shifted then. While Tonye seemed to search for reassurances—Lee's English wasn't always the best, he reminded her, as when he'd mentioned their sister and brother—but she'd also heard a new tension in his voice. His confidence was waning. She was sure of it.

For the rest of the day and into the next, her heartbeat thumped an eerie dirge. She called and called, searching for answers. By the afternoon, she couldn't even recount the people she'd dialed. She'd called Tonye and Obi several times. She'd spoken to Bori and Hajtman, her aunt gasping when she heard the news. She couldn't remember whether she'd called Lee, or if he had called her. She couldn't be sure whether the pattern—worry, call, worry, call—was alleviating her anxiety or worsening it. But there was nothing else to be done.

With an intensity she'd never experienced before, she felt the distance from her family. Worrying through the phone lines at least offered some support. On her own, the stress seemed to scream into the night, an angry howl that taunted her if she dared to close her eyes.

And then, at three o'clock in the morning, nearly two full days after that first horrifying call—nearly two full days of worry and fear and nausea and exhaustion and sleeplessness—came the call she'd been waiting for.

This time Lee knew for certain. And the news was bad. His voice strained, he said, "Your parents are dead."

But the words didn't make sense.

Your parents are dead.

She didn't know how to respond to that sentence. It echoed in her ears.

To quiet the phrase, she murmured the only words that came to mind. "What happened?" Her voice sounded strange. Calm. Far away from her body.

He couldn't answer her question. Your parents are dead. He'd heard indirectly through the Chambers Benin City who had been called by the hospital staff on request of her parents' driver Peter. Your parents are dead. Peter had survived the accident, shaken but mostly unharmed.

She couldn't remember hanging up the phone, but suddenly, she was alone, the room silent and nearly dark.

Your parents are dead.

Her face crumbled, suddenly wet with tears. A sound escaped her lips, a wail that poured out, taking her breath with it. Her head felt full, her legs weak, and she fell onto her sofa.

Her selfless, kind Anyu. Her ambitious, responsible Apu.

She would never see them again.

And she was impossibly, unthinkably alone.

Half a world away from her siblings, from her family in Hungary, from her Opumama and aunt in Port Harcourt, from Lee and anyone who knew her parents, she wept until that strange wail grew familiar. Almost comforting.

She wept until the weeping turned dry and achy, with the sounds of her worry mixed with those of sadness and guilt.

Almost mercifully, beneath its grinding rhythm, another thought persisted. Lee had told her something else. When she'd asked him where her sisters were, he'd responded that he didn't know. Just young teenagers, they needed someone to care for them. They needed their family.

They needed her.

But nobody knew where they were. Not Tonye or Obi. Not Bori or Hajtman. Not Lee or anyone else she could think of.

So with no idea who to call, she dialed Information—in Nigeria, NITEL or Nigerian Telecommunications Limited, the monopoly telephone service provider in the country. A woman at the Benin City location answered, and Ebinimi barely waited for the greeting before she blurted, "I'm looking for my sisters. My parents died. Can you help?! Give me any information. Anything!"

There was a brief silence as her words hung in the air between them. "Ah, sorry!" the woman finally responded. "Very sorry. They are probably at a hospital. Were they in Benin City?"

Unsure of where they were when the accident happened, she told the woman that they'd been traveling from Port Harcourt to Lagos.

"There's a teaching hospital nearby," the woman told her. "They may be there. But we haven't been able to reach any of the hospitals for a few days."

Ebinimi could have screamed. Why were the phones still so unreliable there? How could the hospitals be unreachable? What was she supposed to do now?

Before she could formulate an appropriate response, the woman spoke again. "You know what?" she said. "It's on my way home. I can stop by. If you give me their names, I will see if they are there."

If they'd been in the same room, Ebinimi might have thrown her arms around the woman. Instead, she thanked her and shared the girls' names.

"Call here again tomorrow," the woman said. "Ask for me."

The wait might have felt like a torturous eternity if not for the arrangements that had to be made. While Ebinimi had no idea what should happen next, she knew one thing: with Anyu and Apu dead, the three oldest siblings would need to step in as the younger girls' caretakers.

They were Marika and Terike's parents now.

And the girls needed them.

They needed her.

The hours ticked by, impossibly slowly, until, fingers shaking, she dialed NITEL again. After asking for the woman, she was put on a brief hold, a wait that made her feel as though she might jump out of her skin. She stayed calm, carefully breathing slow in spite of the vibration that strobed through her.

"Hello," came the woman's familiar voice. "They are staying

with a family and are no longer in the hospital. They don't have a phone number, but let me give you the number of their neighbor."

The taste of hope, like ice on a scorching hot day, made her heart sing. After she'd thanked the woman profusely, they hung up, and she eagerly dialed the Benin City number. She shifted her weight as the phone rang in her ear, uncertain of what she would hear at the other end of the line. When a voice answered, she explained the situation.

"Hold on," the neighbor said. "Let me go and get someone from the house." She heard the clack of the phone being set on a hard surface, and, once again, she was alone with her thoughts.

While the moments of waiting drew out longer than she would have liked, the promise of what waited on the other end shifted her energy. She imagined embracing her sisters, crying together, holding them as their mother would have done—holding them as she wished their mother could hold her.

Just as she allowed herself to drift down that path, longing for the reassurance of her mother's voice, she heard someone pick up the phone.

"Szia," came a familiar Hungarian greeting. And in an accent that felt like home, a voice continued, "I am Réka Okonkwo. Your sisters are here. They are safe."

Chapter 30

ROSARY

~

T HE HOSPITAL LOOKED RUN DOWN, Terike thought. The walls were unpainted, and the black metal frames that held up the thin and faded mattresses were chipping. All around her, voices mingled with cold, harsh sounds—the rattle of the metal tables' wheels, the shuffle of shoes on the tile floor, the gasping and moaning and shouting that blended together into one, panicky cry.

She tried to process the buzz of activity around her, but the entire experience felt surreal. Amid the chaos, she was taken to a small room and placed on a metal table next to a small, equipment-covered countertop.

She watched, silent, as her mother and sister were taken to a separate room, separated from her own by a picture window. Barely teenagers, both girls were unsure of what to do and scared beyond anything they'd experienced before. Through the glass that divided them, she saw a nurse approach Marika.

"Please!" her sister screamed. "Leave me! Help my mother!"

Her voice sounded strange. Distant and hoarse and peppered with pitiful little hiccups.

As though in harmony with her sister's screams, her mother moaned. The terrible, low refrain had begun in the car. Now, in the hospital, her mother's pained wails grew softer. And they formed into words. "Help me." Again and again, she repeated the cry.

It was bizarre to know she was there with her mother and sister and to still feel so distant from them. Distant from everything. And as the seconds ticked by in that strange, disjointed realm, her body fell into an unnatural calm. The sounds felt suddenly far away, the silence in her mind wrapping around her like a blanket.

"So," she asked the doctor. "What are you doing?"

The conversation felt casual—almost reassuring—even as he pressed into her aching skull, a long, curved needle grasped between his fingers. She felt eerily calm. Unable to move or form meaningful sentences, she tried to keep her wits about her—to do something that may be useful in a situation that lacked all predictability and control.

"I'm just stitching your head," he replied. "Then I will give you some medicine to put down your swelling."

"Great," she confirmed, staring blankly forward.

The doctor's voice had been calm, the first she'd heard without a trace of dread. It felt good. "How long do you think it will take for the swelling to go down?" She told herself that this was all nearly over. Perhaps she would wait an hour, maybe two, before everything was back to normal—before they could continue to Lagos; the day's activities were interrupted, but still salvageable. She told herself that what she'd just been through wasn't the life-altering accident she'd thought it was.

Instead, in that still, quiet voice, he answered, "It should take some weeks."

Some weeks.

The answer stung more than the stitches. Yet her voice came out as clear and unbothered as it had before. As if someone else had taken over her body. "Oh. Okay."

The response sounded weak to her ears, but it carried a trace of something else, too. In her own voice, she heard the sound of maturity—the type of thoughtful consideration her parents encouraged in her.

They would be so proud.

She would tell them, when she saw them next, how grown up she'd been.

Only a short time earlier—perhaps hours, by now, but no longer—her father had commented on her sister's maturity. She and Marika had been fighting over some silly thing, and her sister had casually applied their mother's lipstick.

Wide-eyed, Terike had looked between her father and her sister, certain Marika would be reprimanded for putting on makeup. They were too young, their parents always said. And no matter how they'd begged, the answer never changed.

But this time, her father had glanced into the backseat and, a smile creeping across his face, remarked, "My daughter is growing up so fast."

She loved her father's smile—loved the feeling of making him proud.

He would certainly be proud of how she was handling things. She was calm and collected. Very grown up.

She couldn't wait to tell him.

At the thought, her stomach flipped.

But why?

Everything was fine. Everything would be fine. It had to be.

But if everything was fine, then why did she feel the need to be so calm? If everything was fine, where was her father? If everything was fine, why were they here, in this chaos, and why was she so intent on reassuring herself that everything was fine?

There was only one answer.

It couldn't be real.

Any moment, her father would arrive to take care of things. Then, they would be on their way.

"Mommy!"

The childlike word escaped her lips before she could process what she'd seen. Her mother, her mommy, was brought past the little operating room where Terike sat, and without a thought, she slid from the table and raced to follow her.

But as she got closer to her mother, she realized the woman was distorted. Anyu didn't look like herself. She didn't look like any person she'd seen before.

Her eyes were swollen and purple. They were too large. Round. Like Homer Simpson's eyes. Her head was half-shaved, with lines of stitches punctuating the bloody scalp.

Could this be Anyu?

Just as Terike let herself wonder, the Rosary, faintly spoken in English, poured repetitively from the woman's lips:

"Hail Mary, full of grace, the Lord is with you.
Blessed are you amongst women and blessed is the fruit of
    Thy womb Jesus.
Holy Mary, mother of God,
Pray for us sinners,

Now and at the hour of our death.

Amen."

Like a familiar melody, the prayer encircled Terike. She relaxed into the feeling. The purple, swollen woman was Anyu. And if Anyu was praying, all would be well. She'd known it all along. Everything would be okay.

Suddenly, a woman's hand grabbed her shoulder. "Lay here," a staff member ordered, pushing Terike out of the way. Staff rushed toward her mother. The woman continued, "Everything will be fine. You need to sleep."

But when she closed her eyes, she heard a roar of activity.

A nightmare, she thought, so she flashed her eyelids open to find, in horror, that the nightmare wasn't in her mind. It was in front of her.

A new burst of adrenaline shot through her exhausted body. Circling her mother's bed, doctors pressed on Anyu's chest. They shouted to one another. With a strange, rhythmic breathing, they murmured as they leaned over her mother, pressing again and again. Their bodies lunged and waited, lunged and waited, lunged and waited, the bed rattling under their weight.

"What's happening?!"

"Nothing," a nurse barked. "Everything is fine. Don't worry. They are helping her. Go back to sleep."

Certain that no nightmare could be worse than this one, she squeezed her eyes closed.

When she opened them again, her mother was gone. The bed she lay in had been stripped to bare, stained, yellow foam.

It was as though her mother had never been there.

Blinking, she held herself still, her shoulder digging through her own foam mattress and into the hard base below.

Where was her mother?

She sat up then, scanning the room. Lined up in two rows, the room housed twenty beds. Her sister was next to her. Marika had a long vertical slice from her hair to her eyebrow. Striped across the cut were little knots.

A few beds over, a woman lay, deathly still, her face puffy like Anyu's. Another woman snored, sleeping in a bed across the aisle. A third groaned quietly.

Where was Anyu?

Where was her mommy?

"She's in another room," a nurse answered, and only then did Terike realize she'd asked the question aloud. "She is fine. Don't worry."

But why would they move her?

She couldn't be more injured than the groaning woman. Certainly, she couldn't be worse than the puffy-faced lady. And the hospital was small. Barely a hospital at all—with blank walls and little supplies—compared to some she'd seen in Hungary. So where would they take her?

At first, she opened her mouth to ask. But, thinking better of it, she let silence fall around her.

Even though their answer was confusing, she preferred it to the one she feared.

Don't think about it, she told herself. They would see their mother soon.

Bold and terrible, a sickening thought nagged at her. It lingered like a gnat in the corner of her swollen eyes, sensed more than seen.

It could be terrible to learn the truth. But it was also terrible not to know.

So, along with Marika, she began to ask, over and over.

"Where is my mother?"

"Oh, both your parents are alive!" a nurse replied, her voice bouncy and light. "They are just in another ward being cared for together!"

They both sighed at that answer. Of course! Everything was fine. She'd known that was probably the case. This was just a strange detour.

But, as a tiny seed of longing grew to a crippling weight of desperation, she soon found that their answers weren't enough. Her mother had been groaning in pain the last time she'd seen her. Her father had looked so still after the accident. Her worry began to consume her. She needed to see her parents.

"Where are my parents?" she asked, this time directing the question to a staff member.

"They have been taken to another town," he answered. "You will see them soon."

"Where is my mommy?"

"They're just next door!"

"Where is my daddy?"

"They will come to pick you up soon."

With each response more illogical than the last, the gnat of worry grew more insistent, its buzzing augmented by the staff's averted gaze and uncomfortable body language.

And then there was her conversation with Peter.

When they'd first arrived, she'd asked him, in that blunt, even voice that had overtaken her when they arrived, "Daddy is dead, isn't he?"

The pause had been sickening.

They'd stared at each other for a moment.

Then, before her eyes, his face crumbled like ancient stone. He nodded miserably, confirming what she'd already known.

But the hospital staff said otherwise. They said all was well.

If her father was dead, then all could not be well. So, surely, her father was not dead.

Everything would be okay.

Even as she thought it, she knew it couldn't be so simple. The competing explanations rubbed against one another, as though begging her to think—to realize what she knew to be true.

She refused.

As long as there was contradiction, there was hope.

And as long as there was hope, things could still go on as they were.

They could still pile back into the car and make their way to Lagos. Joking as he loaded the car, her father would laugh that signature laugh. Her mother, having packed carefully the night before, could gather the things that had scattered by the road in the accident. Loading them back into the car, she would wipe the stray grass and dirt from their suitcases. She would be annoyed at the scuffs but relieved that their things were mostly still intact.

They would eat their snacks. She'd bought groundnuts and plantain chips and a new banana-flavored gum at the corner market street seller.

This time, she wouldn't go to sleep as she had before the crash. This time, she would stay awake, chatting happily in the back seat with her mother. His briefcase on his lap, her father would work on paperwork as he always did on long trips.

His briefcase.

At the thought, her stomach lurched.

The scuffed, black leather peaked out from beneath her bed.

If everything was okay, why did she have her father's briefcase?

Her father had loaded it with nairas to ensure they had what they needed. As her mother often complained, withdrawing funds from Nigerian banks was never easy or fast. They would need money for their embassy appointment and for unexpected expenses along the way.

So her father had brought the briefcase.

Now, she had it.

"This was your father's, so now it's for you," a nurse had said when they arrived at the hospital. "We took the fees for the hospital bills out, and the rest is what is left for you."

This was your father's, she'd said.

This was your father's.

She'd just nodded and waited. In the hours since she received the case, she'd nodded more and waited more, tamping down the dread—or maybe it was something like despair—that settled like a pit in her stomach.

If she could only keep things feeling normal, everything would be fine. She had to go on, focusing on the things she could do in her father's absence. When they were all reunited, he would be so proud. Her mother's hair would grow back, and Anyu's eyes—like her own—would stop swelling.

The doctor had told her some weeks. At the time, the prognosis had seemed unbearably long. But it wasn't so bad: in some weeks, everything would be normal. She just had to wait. She just had to keep behaving in the way she had—the way that would make her parents proud.

So when the president of the Benin Chamber of Commerce stopped by, she sat tall like the teenager she was, even if only barely. She'd never met the man, so she only knew who he was because she'd overheard him when he stopped to talk with the staff.

"Give them whatever food they want," he'd told a nurse. "I will take care of it."

She shook her head at the suggestion. While the gesture was kind, her father would never allow that. He would take care of things when he came back to pick her and Marika up.

Then another man she'd never met came to meet her. His eyes were puffy and red, but not like her mother's had been. With a voice that sounded hoarse and choked, he introduced himself as Mr. Lee and handed them both some food.

"I am your father's business partner," he said.

Terike typically preferred to hide behind her father during business interactions. While her father talked, she tried to stay out of the way.

But her father wasn't here. So she would have to greet this man as Apu would have.

"Yes!" she replied. She delivered the greeting with cheerful ease, just as she'd heard him do many times. "My father has said many great things about you. I am so happy to finally meet you!"

She'd expected a gracious smile. Or, as she'd often seen her father's business relations do, maybe he would extend his hand to her, and she would take it, giving one solid shake.

Instead, he closed his eyes. Tears glistened on his lashes. One rolled down the outside of his face.

So she pressed on. "Did you stop by to see my parents yet?" she asked.

The corners of his mouth trembled and turned downward, his chin wrinkling. He didn't reply. Instead, he looked away from her, just as the hospital staff had done since she arrived. A terrible silence hung in the room, an uncanny vibration that told her not to ask again.

For a moment, they sat like that. Quiet. Still. Horrible. Just when she thought he might crumple forward, he rose from his chair and wished them well.

Mr. Lee had come and gone. The Benin Chambers president, too.

Where were her parents?

With no answers in sight, one final visitor stopped by the hospital.

The woman's green eyes looked sad, and her long hair fell behind her in a thick, gray-streaked braid. When she addressed the girls by name, Terike thought she heard something familiar in her voice. And as she continued in rich, comfortable Hungarian, Terike's longing for her mother threatened to suffocate her.

This woman, Terike realized, was a friend of Anyu's, the mother of the man who had stopped by to visit just a few weeks earlier. As the woman introduced herself, Terike thought of how her mother would be sad to miss seeing her.

With tears in her eyes, Réka said, "I will be taking you to my home today."

Since they'd gotten to the hospital, Terike had nodded and waited, nodded and waited, nodded and waited. Again, she nodded. But this time, she couldn't wait.

Her voice coming out much louder than she'd intended, she blurted, "We don't want to leave without our parents."

"You don't have to go if you don't want to," a nurse offered.

"Okay!" Terike said. "Well, we don't want to! Not without our parents!" The pace and timbre of her voice startled her then, and she thought she might weep. Fighting against the urge, she swallowed hard and planted her feet.

In the battle between her urge to scream and her hard-fought belief that everything would be alright, the only choice was to go with the woman. This woman, more than the hospital workers, gave her hope of a reunion. With each passing day, she'd asked to see her mother over and over, and her hope had dwindled. Now, fine as a delicate, precious thread, a strong breeze could snap it in two.

If Réka's offer promised some renewed hope of seeing her parents, she would greedily accept.

When they reached the woman's home, nothing seemed to change. Days passed without a word between them and Réka's sons and daughter, Roza, who was their age. Each day, as they had since the accident, they asked after their parents. And one afternoon, as Terike napped, she awoke to find Réka sitting at the edge of her bed crying. The girl held as still as possible, waiting for the moment to pass.

But it was that moment—more than Peter's miserable nod, more than Lee's crumpled expression, more than even her mother's desperate prayer—that felt like the final call of a dirge. In that moment, she knew that her instincts had been right all along.

So, the next day, she asked once again—firmly, with all the bravery she could muster—when they would see their parents. Her voice sounded calm, as it had before, but the calmness felt closer. She was no longer looking through the window of that hospital room. Now she was looking at Réka. Réka could tell her the truth.

Her words thick and heavy, Réka replied, "Go sit in the room with Marika. I have to talk to you both."

Terike's heart raced then, the jolt of energy as hot and fierce as it had ever been. She did as she was told.

The minutes passed like hours until the woman appeared in the doorway. She walked into the bedroom, slowly pushed the door closed behind her, and sat between them on the bed. She embraced the two girls as if they were her own.

"Your parents will be in the hospital longer than we expected," she said. After a strangled inhale, she continued, "Your father died in the car."

Terike knew the words she would speak next. And while she willed them not to come, they felt inevitable. Both impossible and unbearably real.

"Your mother died in the hospital. Later that day."

A wave of release flooding through her body, Terike and her sister fell into the woman's arms and wept.

EPILOGUE

As he gazed from the plane's window, Tonye reflected on how the world below, obscured by pillowy white clouds, had transformed itself over the past few weeks. So many of his life's changes had been marked by travel.

He hadn't been in Nigeria in a long time.

Now, for the second time in just a few weeks, he traveled back to the place he'd called home for much of his childhood. Like the last time, Anyu wouldn't be beside him with her warm embrace and gentle ear. Neither would Apu greet him inquiring about his studies with a curiosity that revealed his pride in his children.

In early August, just a few days after the accident, he'd made the first of two trips to Nigeria. Obi and their older cousin, Olaf had accompanied him to Benin City while Hajtman, Bori's husband, went to the Hungarian Embassy in Lagos to see that the girls had their passports and could leave Nigeria without problems.

Dr. Okonkwo had greeted them at the airport and taken them the short distance to his home. When they'd arrived, the girls had bolted from the house, grinning and shouting their brothers' names as they plunged into their arms.

Tonye had paused at his sisters' appearances. Terike's face was swollen, eyes narrowed to a squint. Both girls wore white bandages around their heads, covering what he later learned was a long, arched slice along the top of Terike's scalp and a shorter, though more visible, vertical cut on Marika's forehead. Dr. Okonkwo had removed Terike's stitches.

Despite their injuries, the girls had seemed so genuinely happy to see them that, for just a brief, fleeting second, everything seemed okay. Ensuring the girls' safety had been their purpose. And that purpose, even if only for a moment, outweighed the pain.

Soon after that impossibly joyful reunion, Marika and Terike had been whisked away to Budapest. Tonye remained behind to make the necessary arrangements for his parents' estate.

He sifted through his parents' things, his father's business paperwork and political campaign items filed alongside his mother's growing collection of creative writing.

As he reflected on this lost time, he was comforted by the loving words of his mother. A dedication addressed her words directly to him—to all three of her oldest children, "A Letter to the Big Ones":

"The morning is still cold; it is dark, four o'clock,
Your father leaves me just around this time with a kiss,
I can still sleep, but he carries water,
Outside from the garden tap, while the neighbor rests!

It is dark; nobody sees what he is doing,
The dog is outside; it calls if it finds a snake,
But we hope there will not be such peril,
Mr. Eche's flowers those would have to be frightened!

At five I also wake up, cheerfully if there is power,
In the computer is Apu's work at this time,
A lot of tasks, we are enjoying this modern device,
For a little mental exercise it certainly comes handy!"

In the kitchen the yeast has already risen,
It is cleaner, and cheaper than the bread I have to buy,
It is also simpler, also well-liked, just don't find out its secret,
They dust it off, and blow around its crust by mouth!

After I roll the kifli I fry yellow plantains,
I cut them lengthwise and across, finally I beat eggs,
In little oil, for scrambled eggs, for the little girls' snack,
With chocolate milk for breakfast, we devour in abundance!

At six o'clock out of bed Marika, Terike,
Warm water your father has already mixed to readiness,
Candle if you need don't be afraid, we are here nearby,
I will set the table you just dress up meanwhile!"

As he continued reading, it was joy that leapt out at him, the realization of how truly happy she was to have spent twenty-five years—since they'd first met in the summer of 1972 in Budapest—with the man she loved.

Tonye made his way from the plane to the airport and onto the city streets. He wouldn't head to the familiar estate that had been his childhood home. This trip, instead, took him to the home of family friends, the Wadas, where he would stay as he took the final steps to lay his parents to rest.

Tonye could sense that his parent's life impacted others in

Nigeria, and not only those they knew. In Port Harcourt, he'd been surprised to hear multiple radio reports of his father's death as Chambers President. Later in the trip, he'd seen a thirty-minute television news program in which the death of his father shared time with that of Fela Kuti, a well-known Afrobeat singer.

He prepared himself for the expected exhaustion and stress. They had two wake keepings planned—one at the Port Harcourt estate and a second at the guest house his father had built in Tombia—followed by their burial on that precious family land.

When the first event finally arrived, he found himself over-whelmed, instead, by the display of his parents' remarkable legacies. The plastic, rainbow-striped tent overflowed with people, from very old friends to people he had never met before.

Tonye sat next to Chief Rufus Ada George, adorned in his sig-nature top hat, the man who had served as Rivers State's second governor. Ada George's attendance would have meant a lot to Apu, Tonye thought, but even more so, it offered a powerful symbolic message of his father's work—he'd long fought for political unity and anti-corruption. As an NRC candidate, Ada George's presence and speech at the funeral demonstrated the lasting impact of his father's political career.

All around them sat Nigerwives, nuns and priests, friends, and neighbors. Spilling out from the tent and onto the veranda, the many people his parents' lives had touched joined together in commemoration, many offering heartfelt speeches of tribute.

The next morning, they'd held a funeral mass at Corpus Christi Catholic Church followed by a long drive through treacherous ter-rain to Tombia, to the Saviors Anglican Church, where a solemn, closed-casket funeral service was held.

From there, they'd traveled by a short, rutted road to the house

Matthew had built. Just as the Port Harcourt estate had been flooded with friends and family, it seemed like the entire village had come out that day.

Despite the quiet, somber tone, a large crowd surrounded the house, most dressed in colorful traditional attire.

His throat felt dry, tight with the finality of the moment, a moment that became more final when, following the wake, his parents were manually lowered into the ground. A few men jumped in and supported the caskets. Crowds gathered around, watching as Tonye laid the wreath and threw the first soil.

The experience was surreal. A weight like nothing he'd ever felt before settled over him like a cloud, only shouldered by the condolences of friends and relatives.

Despite the day's emotional weight, the intense anxiety he'd expected never materialized. Instead, as he looked out over this land, he felt oddly calm. It had meant so much to his parents, this place. Apu had dreamed of this land, of a retirement close to family, in the heart of the region that had been his home for so much of his childhood and adolescence.

Standing on this land in Tombia, Tonye was immediately transported back to the last time he'd been in the Riverine region—also the last visit Anyu had made. She'd worked for some time to make books available to the poor Ijaws of the Riverine region, at one point even converting one of the bedrooms in their home into a library.

But the project they'd been working on when they were last in the Riverine together was bigger—or, at least, more exciting.

A helicopter had come to pick them up—a thrilling experience—so they could deliver boxes of books to a local secondary school in Brass. The Nigerwives had organized the project, and they were warmly greeted by the school.

In a way, then, this place symbolized both Tonye's parents' passions—his father's deep investment in improving the politics of the Riverine region, and his mother's determination to help educate children. The land would not give his parents rest in the retirement they'd hoped for, but here they would rest, surrounded by the symbols of their lives' work.

Despite the ache in his chest, despite the heavy longing he felt to spend just one more day with them, he felt at peace.

While these services were important, the priority had always been for his sisters—to ensure their care, to give them the best lives they could have, and to support them through the unthinkable trauma they'd experienced.

The decision of their permanent home had only recently been resolved.

Soon after the accident, Nagymami had brought the issue to Tonye. She had taken her daughter and son-in-law's deaths very hard, but had gained strength when she was reminded that her grandchildren needed her motherly support.

Her impulse to care for the children only raised the specter of helplessness in her. When the idea of bringing Marika and Terike to live at the Zsombolyai Street apartment had come up, she'd become distraught, pulling Tonye aside for a serious conversation.

"They cannot live here with us," she told him tearfully, "I would have to raise them. At my age, I cannot do this."

While she prided herself on doing everything she could to help her family, at ninety years old, she wasn't always able to care even for herself, relying on her daughter and delivery services for her meals. She certainly could not raise two teenagers.

Others had stepped forward to fill the gap, offering their homes as options. An older cousin, Edó, and her husband, Lajos, asked to raise them—they'd raised five children of their own and joked that two more would be a cinch. Aci and her husband Zoli, Marika and Terike's godparents, were also willing to care for them, despite being in their sixties.

But the tug at the siblings' hearts was to keep the girls close. They should live with family, the closer the better. So, while Ebinimi was just twenty-one years old, she would soon graduate from college and insisted that the sisters—all three of them—stay together.

It was fitting, in a way—the teenagers had so looked forward to moving to the US, a dream they'd shared with their parents. Although Judit and Matthew's dream had been shattered by tragedy, in this small way, their plans could live on, one small piece of their legacy.

His parents' legacy. That was perhaps the thought that stuck most with Tonye as he reflected on the past weeks' events. His parents had left behind so much in their lives—so many people touched by the good they'd done.

Surely that was demonstrated by the crowds who had joined him to mourn, first in Port Harcourt and then in Tombia for the burial on September 6. In Budapest, the little chapel on Ulászló Street had overflowed with love for his parents—the day Princess Diana was buried and a day after Mother Teresa's death.

They would be in good company in heaven.

And their memories would persist on earth.

Like tributaries flowing outward from a central waterway, the lives they'd touched were too many to enumerate.

His spirit full from the celebration of his parents' lives, Tonye made his way to the Budapest Ferihegy International Airport where, once again, all five siblings came together, embracing in shared grief and love.

The road ahead would be neither all good nor all bad. In the coming years, their lives would pose challenges and proffer opportunities, weaving and winding ahead of them with the grandeur of the Danube and the resourcefulness of the Niger.

As their parents before them, they would endure the world's fallout and embrace its blessings.

As their parents before them, they would step boldly forward into their new lives.

And so, just as it had for their parents before them, the universe opened its arms wide.

ABOUT THE AUTHOR

DANIEL MAMAH, MD is a physician and Professor of Psychiatry at Washington University School of Medicine in St. Louis, Missouri, and a Distinguished Fellow of the American Psychiatric Association. He graduated from Federal Government College in Port Harcourt, Nigeria, and Semmelweis Medical School in Budapest, Hungary. Dr. Mamah was the founding president of the Missouri Psychiatric Association and served on the Diagnostic and Statistical Manual of Mental Disorders – Fifth Edition (DSM-5) Task Force. A leading researcher on psychosis in the United States and Africa, he has published multiple articles and book chapters. He has lived in Hungary, England, and Nigeria, and now resides in the United States with his wife, Thelma, and two daughters, Caroline and Sophia.